A FRENZY
OF
MERCHANTMEN

A FRENZY
OF
MERCHANTMEN

Brian Callison

COLLINS
St James's Place, London
1977

William Collins Sons & Co Ltd
London · Glasgow · Sydney · Auckland
Toronto · Johannesburg

First published 1977
© Brian Callison 1977
ISBN 0 00 222239–6
Set in Baskerville
Made and Printed in Great Britain by
William Collins Sons & Co Ltd Glasgow

Part One

The Reason Why

She was a Type 81, 1st Rate general purpose frigate.

She was also 360 feet long and of some 2300 tons displacement, while her combined steam and gas turbine engines forced her through the water at a speed which – were she travelling in a built-up area – would have had every traffic patrolman in sight fumbling admonishingly for his note-book.

But *Tribal* Class warships of the Royal Navy avoid the possibility of navigating over land like the very plague, while the only things which build up around seventy miles nor'-east by north of Muckle Flugga in the Shetlands are anti-cyclones, depressions, and a surfeit of thirty foot waves which come roaring out of the blackness, hissing contemptuously at sailormen aboard their bucketing slivers of ships and sometimes even killing them – just to prevent complacency from creeping into the latitudes of the Norwegian Sea.

Certainly there were no thirty foot waves on that grey, uninspiring morning. Just restless little ten foot ones reaching up aggressively to buffet, disintegrate, and tumble back impotently into their white foam shrouds under the expressing flare of the frigate's bow. Yet even then, while conscious of his temporary superiority over the Norwegian Sea, there was still no complacency in the mind of the frigate's captain – only tension . . . Because this was the swinging seventies, and all the world at peace – or quite a lot of it, anyway – which made his task a rather delicate one.

For he was instructed to perform an Act of War.

And against a maritime power which could muster more

admirals than the Royal Navy could produce . . . say . . . missiles?

But there wasn't only the tension that twisted uneasily in the pit of the frigate captain's belly on that morning. There was also another kind of tension in the cold air – the International kind. The kind which builds up between two countries when one of them suddenly discovers that reciprocal cultural visits and the interchange of State orchestras aren't quite in harmony with the maintenance of a large force of unemployed and unmotivated fighting troops.

Whereupon all the fleet admirals and field-marshals and airforce commanders, who infinitely prefer controlling readyuse ICBMs to joining the Retired List, press urgently for a little less of the velvet glove and a little more thumping of the discreetly mailed fist.

Which was why, ten days before, the mailed fist – in the shape of a Soviet *Krupnyi* Class destroyer – had thumped down on a rather bemused British freighter called the *Pentland Firth* as she steamed, in absolute innocence, across the sixty-second parallel of northern latitude, *en route* for the flesh-pots of Reykjavik.

And why the frigate with the tense captain and the White Ensign was steaming, somewhat more predatorily, through these spiteful ten foot waves of the Norwegian Sea.

It wasn't so much the seriousness of the *Pentland Firth* affair. After all, they'd only signalled her to stop and receive a boarding party who had – after two hours of being called 'Bloody pirates' and 'Soddin' Reds' by an intractably morose British master – disconcertingly returned to the Soviet destroyer without giving any clear reason for their coming in the first place . . . No, it was more the fact that a vessel under the British Flag had been illegally detained while going about her traditional business in International Waters.

And nobody tampers with the traditions of the British Navy. Except the British Government.

So the British Government, deciding that an 'eye for an eye' response was the only way to bring the Soviets to a true understanding of our determination, proposed three grave courses of action.

Firstly, they sent a strong note of protest to the Embassy of the USSR, Kensington Palace Gardens, w.8.

Next, they summarily ordered the immediate cancellation of a courtesy visit to Leningrad by the massed pipes and drums of The Black Watch.

And, finally, they dispatched a *Tribal* Class frigate from Rosyth to patrol the grey wastes of the Norwegian Sea.

Her mission . . .? To seek out, stop, board, and then – having established a principle – release the first Russian merchantman she chanced upon.

But, for Christ's sake – in the *nicest* possible way!

For three days Her Majesty's Frigate *Afghan* had laboured gloomily on a series of reciprocal courses, leaving an almost permanent groove in the sea area between the Faeroes and the approaches to Kristiansund. And then, at 0731 zulu time on the morning of the fourth day, the officer of the watch called the Captain to the bridge.

'We have another contact, sir. Bearing red four five relative, range twenty-three miles and closing.'

The Captain nodded unenthusiastically. They'd had a lot of contacts over the past seventy-two hours but all of them under the flags of the NATO Alliance.

'Port fifteen, cruising revolutions both engines . . . Course to intercept, please?'

A haze of spray spattered over the bridge windows as the bow swung into the sea. The Captain climbed heavily into his chair while the frigate settled on to her new heading. 'Here we go again,' he thought, 'David and the elusive Goliath. Now, if this was the Med there'd be more Soviet shipping around than seagulls. But that's when you *don't* damn well want to be watched every time a rating goes to the bloody heads . . .'

They made visual contact with the approaching vessel fourteen minutes later. She was a merchantman.

The speaker above the Captain's head crackled electronically with a trace of Welsh accent. 'Bridge – Radar! Contact bearing zero zero thuree. Heading wun seven fi-yiv true, range . . . ah . . . eight point two miles and closing. Contact's speed eighteen knots, sir!'

The Captain raised his binoculars. 'Come right five degrees to three five seven! What d'you make of her, Number One?'

The First Lieutenant moved in behind the Captain's chair. The rain squall which had partly obscured the target ship cleared and she slid starkly into the ten magnification of his eyepieces. 'Deep sea trader, sir. Ten, twelve thousand tons, just an ordinary dry cargo ship. Could be any nationality until we clear her centrecastle and pick out her Colours.'

'Call her on the lamp. Ask what ship!' The Captain lit a cigarette and pulled a face, it annoyed him to think that Number One had stopped smoking three weeks ago while he'd been trying to for years and never actually got around to keeping it up. And there'd been that indefinable trace of smugness ever since. Even superiority? The Aldis lamp chattered interrogatively . . . A . . . A . . . A . . . A . . . the call to an unknown station.

The communications rating half turned his head. 'She's not acknowledging, sir. Shall I send K?'

'I wish to communicate with you?' The Captain drew hard on the cigarette, eyes searching the First Lieutenant's face for the first hint of deprecation. 'No!' he said positively. 'Belay the transmission!'

He swung round to face the First Lieutenant. 'They're being deliberately evasive. Any ship of that size must have a watchkeeper on her bridge . . . I intend to treat her as hostile.'

He glanced back to where the freighter plugged stolidly towards them under the grey overcast. The tension was churning in his belly once more – maybe it was the use of the word 'hostile'. He'd have to watch that – contacts were really only hostile or friendly when there was a war on. But then again, if he made the wrong move in the next few minutes, there just could be anyway . . . Folding the half-smoked Players into the ashtray he said slowly, 'Sea dutymen if you please, Number One.'

The First Lieutenant raised the microphone and hesitated. 'Gun's crew, sir?'

'Not yet. We'll run down her port side and take a look at her Colours.'

'Aye, aye, sir!' The First Lieutenant snapped the call button. 'Special sea dutymen, close up . . .! Special sea dutymen, close up!'

A wave, slightly larger than the rest, reached up and slapped the black-painted 'F' on the ship's side warningly. They felt the slight tremor as far down as the engine control-room, but no one thought it strange that a ship should shiver.

They swept regally down the freighter's side with a gap of precisely one sea mile between the two ruler-straight wakes. The First Lieutenant eagerly scanned the snowy-white superstructure and, in odd contrast, the rust-scarred, once black hull for any signs which would indicate the contact's country of origin.

Slowly at first, then faster and faster, the gap between the merchantman's masts opened as the frigate surged abeam until, suddenly, the high poop came clear of the intervening deckhousings and the First Lieutenant felt the Captain lean forward slightly.

'She's Russian!' The Captain said quietly, 'Close up "A" Gun, if you please. Armament broadside.'

The Number One's voice was steady over the piped broadcast. 'Close up "A" Gun's crew. Gunnery Officer to the bridge!' He released the microphone button and watched the ratings running along the spray-dappled fore-deck, hours of training further accelerated by a desire to reach the shelter of the gunshield.

The Captain lit another cigarette defiantly. So this was what they called 'The Crunch'? The moment when he, and only he, had to make a decision which could conceivably light the blue touch paper for the world's last war. Or did he? His orders were there in black and white . . . 'Stop and board, using the minimum of force' . . . He smiled fractionally through the spiralling smoke. Perhaps there was a Soviet admiral somewhere over that bleak horizon who would issue *his* frigate captains with similarly worded orders when the Red freighter screamed and the time for reprisals was due – except that *their* minimum might be delivered along the subsonic parabola of a *Styx* missile. It was all a matter of degree, really . . .

The talkback system crackled. ' "A" Gun's crew closed up!'

'Thank you,' the Captain said politely, allowing his eyes to sweep that intervening water again. The sea was getting up, lumpier now than it had been even twenty minutes ago. Bloody northern latitudes. Now the Med, that was the place . . . except for those damned Soviet Fleet Units, of course. He turned to the Gunnery Officer. 'Carry on please, Guns. I intend to come round now and run down her port side, fifteen cables off . . . Communicator?'

'Sir?'

'Hoist "I intend to communicate by means of International Code". Allow them three minutes to acknowledge, then replace it with SQ3 irrespective.'

The signalman bent over the flag locker just as the Captain caught the First Lieutenant's eye. He fought, and lost, the temptation to be patronizing. '. . . SQ3, Number One. "You should stop or heave to; I am going to board you." '

The First Lieutenant answered 'Yessir!' quite cheerfully. He'd known that already but it didn't matter. He didn't *smoke* any more either.

'Both engines ahead full. Starboard fifteen. Steady on . . .' The Captain glanced astern to where the Russian still plodded along on her original dead-straight southerly heading. It made him feel uncomfortable, the way she just ignored their existence. Almost as if the Royal Navy didn't mean anything any more. He shrugged irritably, '. . . steady on one seven five!'

The ship shivered again. But of course it was only the sea under her swinging bow.

The gunlayer on 'A' Gun was a man who liked bacon rind. In fact he liked it so much that, to him, the rest of the rasher was just packing. In the mess-deck they called him Pigskin because, while his oppo's carefully saved their best until last – the fatty bits or the lean, or even the golden blob of yolk – Pigskin would dissect, isolate and preserve his rind with the supreme craftsmanship of a senior pathologist. To Pigskin the flavourful crispy laces were as the shark's fin to the Oriental, or the sheep's mournful eye to a Bedouin gastronome.

Which was why the GL2's jaws were champing rhythmically as he settled in the gunlayer's seat, practised hands caressing the laying handles expertly. And also why the PO Captain of the Mounting sniffed disparagingly to no one in particular, and muttered, 'Should be *USS* 'stead've HMS . . . him chewin' all the bloody time like that!'

Then it was all smooth, rehearsed action in the turret of 'A' Gun as the Gunnery Officer's voice snapped the range, bearing and target description from the vacantly open mouth of the loudspeaker.

'Target! Range, thuree thousand yards: Bearing, zero fi-yiv fi-yiv degrees . . . Intend to shoot two cables ahead of merchant ship, starboard side!'

Pigskin felt the mounting swing smoothly as the gun traversed on, then his right eyebrow buffered into the cushioning foam rubber of the gunlayer's telescope as he concentrated on maintaining the level horizon, compensating for the now considerable roll of the frigate's corkscrewing through the rising beam sea.

Pigskin had one primary function at this juncture – to keep the 4.5 inch rifled bore of 'A' Gun's long barrel at a constant elevation despite anything the Norwegian Sea could do to deflect him.

And if chewing helped, then the hell with Petty Officer QA 1's!

'Bridge – AIO! We're picking up a WT transmission on UHF, sir. Very strong! Five letter code groups, we're taping them for analysis later.'

The Captain spoke without lowering his glasses. 'She's shouting for help then, Number One.'

'Still not speaking to us though, sir. Are you going to jam her signals?'

'No!' The Captain swung round in his chair. 'Make to Flag Officer, info MOD Navy . . . Immediate! Contact now identified as Soviet merchant ship *Kuibyshev*, break . . .' He glanced up at the bulkhead clock. Seven minutes would bring them to a nice round time-group for lighting a fuse.

'. . . I intend to open fire at 08.30 hours zulu time!' the Captain finished. And lit another cigarette.

'Coded signal, sir?' The Officer of the Watch sounded a little overawed.

'Plain language, if you please.' The Captain grinned at the First Lieutenant's raised eyebrow. He felt better now, a lot better. The decision had been taken and they were committed for better or for worse. Now there was only the tradesman's part of the operation to complete.

'Plain language, Number One,' the Captain reiterated. 'If the Red sailor over there is listening – and you can bet your old boots to an admiral's epaulette he is – then he might just gather that we aren't playing bluff poker . . . Have a cigarette?'

The First Lieutenant stretched out an unthinking hand, then drew it away hurriedly. Aware of the reproachful stare in his junior's eye the Captain swallowed his disappointment and murmured deceitfully, 'I do apologize,

Robert. I'd quite forgotten you'd stopped.'

The clock on the bulkhead said 8.26 a.m. GMT. The Navy called it 'zulu time'.

The Gunnery Officer stiffened. ' "A" Gun on bearing. Range set, sir!'

'Solid shot, if you please.'

The talkback switch bounced an electronically amplified snick around the steel- and glass-encased bridge. ' "A" Gun! One practise round . . . *Load!*'

'Hoist SQ1!'

The Captain raised his binoculars again. He had gambled on the Russian's showing some signs of movement by now, especially after his last signal, yet there still wasn't a damned sign of anyone on the big freighter's bridge. It was sheer bloody frustration, almost like a moth battering at an inanimate lamp shade. And SQ1 was the only thing he had left to threaten with – three little coloured flags which said, peremptorily, YOU SHOULD STOP OR HEAVE TO, OTHERWISE I SHALL OPEN FIRE ON YOU!

' "A" Gun loaded, sir!'

The red sweep hand on the clock seemed to surge a little faster. It raced up to the vertical, establishing the time as being 08.28 zulu.

The two ships slammed side by side through the grey water, separated by one and a half sea miles and an infinite difference of language, politics and attitudes. Aboard the sleek frigate with the streaming White Ensign the only sign that anything was amiss was the long threatening finger of 'A' Gun forward, trained fifty-five degrees to starboard of her fore and aft line, and aimed precisely four hundred yards ahead of the rust-flecked bow of a ship called after one of the forty-nine provinces of the Russian Soviet Federal Socialist Republic – the merchantman *Kuibyshev*.

And aboard the *Kuibyshev* there was absolutely no indication that anything was amiss at all.

It was very disconcerting.

Suddenly the First Lieutenant stiffened involuntarily.

There *was* a movement at last, over there on the freighter's after-deck. A solitary figure moving aft, towards the high poop. Climbing now, then making his way casually and unhurriedly along the port alleyway to where the red flag stood out board flat in the head wind.

The Captain gripped his binoculars just a little tighter. Reprieve? Were they actually going to . . .? The lonely black figure halted at the base of the staff and appeared to be fumbling with the flag halyard. The Captain half turned. 'Have someone stand by the Ensign, she's going to dip her Colours to us. Quickly now!'

He grinned at the First Lieutenant, a trace of relief evident in his eye. 'Seems we won't need the gun after all, Number One. Must confess I'm damn glad, too, but as she's offering her respects she's also presumably going to heave to . . .' He glanced at the clock. One minute to go. '. . . They cut it damned fine, all the same.'

The flag with the five-pointed star surmounting the hammer and sickle dropped sharply to the base of the staff. The First Lieutenant raised his voice slightly. '*Dip!*'

He watched as the White Ensign was lowered, then immediately raised again. Swinging back on the Russian he waited for her to follow suit by completing the normal courtesy and rehoisting hers. The single Soviet sailor appeared to hesitate briefly and then – with the First Lieutenant's eyes growing wider and wider in outraged disbelief – the man tucked a rolled-up bundle under his arm, raised a hand in what was unmistakably another rather less formal, but still indisputably International gesture, and sauntered away from a now denuded ensign staff.

'My God!' The First Lieutenant grated shakily, 'The bastards have removed their Colours completely. We . . . We've dipped to a bloody merchantman. A bloody *cargo* boat . . .!'

The Captain didn't comment, because the tension was back with a vengeance. Only this time it was mixed with anger. And maybe even a little hatred.

So he just said, flatly, 'Gunnery Officer! One round . . .
Fire!'

Virtually isolated from the rest of the outside world by the
thin grey steel of the gunshield, the crew of 'A' Gun Mounting
weren't able to view the little bit of the Norwegian Sea which
rolled and tumbled between the two speeding ships. Even
had they been able to, it wouldn't really have made any
difference to the outcome, although some of them might at
least have noticed casually that, at a point some fifty degrees
to their right, the broken water was becoming even more
broken and that the waves weren't so much waves any
more as just humps and mounds and jagged peaks.

Though when the Gunnery Officer's remote voice,
deliberately steady, irrevocably committed Her Majesty's
Ship *Afghan* to an act of aggression, the crew of 'A' Gun
wouldn't have noticed anything less than a thermo-nuclear
explosion outside their shiny metal environment. Not even
casually.

' "A" Gun! One round . . . *Fire!*'

The Captain of the Mounting sucked in a deep breath.
'*FIIIIRE!*'

Pigskin hunched a little lower in the gunlayer's seat, also
sucking in a deep breath of concentration until, with
devastating impact, a minute fragment of supra-masticated
bacon rind – carried aft on a hurricane of inhalation –
ricocheted from the tip of his uvula, through his open and
unprepared epiglottis, to slam agonizingly to rest in an
involuntarily convulsing trachea.

Or, as Pigskin protested to a shattered Captain of the
Mounting a little later, 'Christ, but I choked, PO. I tell you I
fuckin' well *choked* . . .!'

It was the first link in a chain of circumstances which, over
the succeeding milliseconds of time, were to cause a captain
to lose his ship and a ship to lose its captain.

When 'A' Gun Mounting of Her Majesty's Type 81
General Purpose Frigate *Afghan* finally fired on an unarmed

unit of the Soviet Fleet at precisely zero eight three zero hours and twenty-two seconds.

Zulu time.

In order to prevent a shell turning end over end after it leaves the muzzle of a gun the barrel is rifled, or spirally grooved. This imparts a gyroscopic action to the projectile, causing it to spin from left to right when viewed from the gunlayer's end as it supersonics towards its target.

As the practise round left the muzzle of 'A' Gun it, too, was spinning quite controllably clockwise. Also – being a practise round – it contained no explosive material because the Royal Navy feels that, when HM ships are forced to fire a shot across the bows of a recalcitrant suspect, the primary intention is to scare the hell out of them without actually blowing them out of the water.

But the Norwegian Sea just didn't know the Royal Navy's views on dispatching cautionary shots across the bows of other vessels.

The increasingly broken water just ahead of and between the two ships, lumped irritably on a dead straight line projected from 'A' Gun's traversed barrel to the point of aim ahead of the freighter *Kuibyshev* at precisely the moment when the sliver of bacon rind impacted in Pigskin's windpipe. It was also the moment when the 4.5 inch diameter shell spiralled finally through the super-heated, expanding gasses of the muzzle flash.

It was also the moment when the suffocating GL 2's concentration faltered, when the frigate rolled shudderingly and unexpectedly to starboard under a sneak attack by the grey sea on her quarter, and when the long barrel dipped sharply downwards. It meant that the shell's trajectory was several degrees lower than had been intended.

The shot from *Afghan* struck the water some three hundred yards short of its aiming point ahead of the Russian's bow – that patch of water which was, by then, rearing and leaping in an almost anticipatory frenzy.

The Norwegian Sea acted with the calculated contempt that only the elements can muster. A green-and-white flecked shoulder of the monster clawed skywards, lunging spitefully towards the converging round from 'A' Gun. The shell struck . . . the sea shrugged with cold anger . . . and the projectile – still gyrating from left to right with the hum of a rogue buzz saw – ricocheted crazily away from its intermediate point of impact on a trajectory some forty degrees to the right of its pre-ordained track.

And punched a friction-blackened hole four and a half inches in diameter through the forward face of the Soviet merchantman's wheelhouse.

It continued its rather unorthodox passage by exiting via the after bulkhead of the Russian after first removing the Captain's samovar of early morning tea, the Captain's left leg from the patella down, and the Captain's favourite barometer. In that order.

Captain Viktorovich Mikhail Pritytsky of the Soviet Merchant Marine died from severe surgical, aggravated by intense patriotic, shock at precisely 11.31 hours.

Moscow time.

The Captain of Her Majesty's Ship *Afghan* impassively watched his career disintegrate along with the front of the *Kuibyshev*'s bridge, and said slowly, 'Damn it!'

The First Lieutenant didn't say anything this time. He just numbly lit the cigarette the Captain absent-mindedly passed to him.

While the Norwegian Sea winked happily as the sun came out for the first time that month.

One

'. . . so they hit her.' McReadie said cheerfully, 'Silly bastards!'

I grinned encouragingly. Being Merchant Navy I always got a spiteful boost from hearing that the RN had managed to make a shambles of something, especially when it was an RN commander who was doing the knocking.

Oh, not that you'd call McReadie typical of the average, clean-cut Naval officer, mind. Not like those ruggedly salty young men who stare at you invitingly from the pages of the Sunday supplements, about to leap straight from the bridge of the Polaris submarine that You Too Could Command into a conveniently parked sports car below.

No. McReadie was more of a . . . well . . . a Dartmouth-educated thug, for instance. And driven ruthlessly by the same patriotic single-mindedness of purpose which had already killed a lot of men.

Which made him just like me – Brevet Cable.

Except that my education was more fo'c'slehead practical, and my own love of country further stimulated by the extras to a chief officer's salary which they paid me for assisting in McReadie's little bits of mayhem. But taxable, mind you. In the same way as a prostitute's earnings.

I said, 'And then what?'

He moved across the Senior Officer's (Seagoing) Washroom and stood beside me, fiddling with his tie. 'They boarded the Russian anyway. Even took the frigate's surgeon commander as a goodwill gesture, but her Old Man didn't want to know.'

'They'd ruffled his Soviet pride?' I suggested.

McReadie shrugged indifferently. 'No! They'd shot his

leg off. He was dead.'

I chewed my lip pensively, aware of the faintest ringing of a warning bell somewhere at the back of my mind. When McReadie volunteered any information at all it usually meant that Chief Officer Brevet Cable was about to become involved, and shooting Russian sea captains with four and a half inch diameter bullets was one hell of a way to go about slapping the world's second biggest navy across the face with a challenging gauntlet.

I just had to hope they were only the world's second best, too. Being a natural coward also makes you an optimist. I muttered nervously, 'Which is why I'm here, at Head Office? 'Cause there's a flap on and you need me to get you and the Navy out?'

'No, Mate. There is a flap on, but we *don't* need you . . .' McReadie stood back from the mirror and smoothed his lapels critically, then grinned sardonically at my reflection.

'. . . That's why you're here, Cable boy. Because you *are* expendable.'

I had one special four-letter word to describe McReadie. That was B – O – S – S.

He was also Operations Superintendent of the British Mutual Steam Navigation Company, which made him the most unorthodox serving officer ever spawned out of the Ministry of Defence (Navy) and, incontrovertibly, the most sophisticatedly groovy buccaneer since Drake hung up his bowls long enough to add fireships to the Royal Navy's weapons system.

Though, on reflection, we were all pretty unconventional people in BMSNC. And all of us a bit inclined towards violence – so long as it was directed against Britain's cold war enemies, and that it could be conducted surreptitiously from the Company's somewhat specialized – but still apparently innocuous – dry cargo ships as they went about their legal trading in other people's waters.

And there, in a nutshell, you had the reason for, and the

beautiful simplicity behind, the concept of the British Mutual Steam Navigation Company . . . the single fact that a freighter under the Red Ensign is permitted access to virtually every port in the Atlas, while the rather more obviously aggressive warships of the Royal Navy patrol the deep sea shipping lanes, polish their guns patiently for the day when they may be needed – and stay a long and un-provocative way from the shores of any Eastern Power.

It wasn't sporting. It wasn't at all 'nice', even in a world where the great Powers sit back aloofly and let the little people like the Vietnamese and the Israelis and the Arabs do their hot war self-mutilation for them – but, by God, it was one way of maintaining a British Naval presence which not only eased the taxpayer's burden but showed a National profit as well.

So it was the Company's *British Sailor* which regrettably collided with, and sank, the Russian tanker *Novorossiisk* some twenty-five miles off the east coast of Scotland. In view of the sad lack of Soviet survivors the International Courts had no option but to accept the BMSNC claim that it had been the Russian master's negligence which had caused the disaster and, accordingly, award damages totalling several hundred thousand New Roubles to compensate for the thirty thousand tons of northern Caucasus oil which fouled every Scottish beach from Fife Ness to Aberdeen.

It had the incidental effect of also preventing a rendezvous between the good ship *Novorossiisk* and a fleet of fuel-starved Polish spy trawlers who were scheduled to attend an in-telligence-gathering preview of the Navy's latest ship-to-air missile trials.

Or there was that time when the Chinese People's Republican minelayer *Ch'eng Yang* put down a very efficient lay of contact mines intended to discourage British merchant-men from trading between Hong Kong and Taiwan – then came back the next night to consolidate the job, only to run smack into what was presumed to have been one of her own high explosive eggs.

Well of course, everyone *said* it must have been one of the *Ch'eng Yang*'s own mines, broken from its original moorings by inexplicable means, because the only other ship near that area of the China Sea during the preceding twenty-four hours had been a BMSNC innocent called *British Venturer* – and the inscrutable faces of *Venturer*'s crewmen would have made the Red Orientals look like candidates for the Laugh-in of the Year Award.

Then there was the intriguing suggestion that the loss of the submarine *Ulyanovsk* off Cape Wrath after a painstaking survey of our convoy assembly anchorages-to-be had actually been caused by a – later quickly removed – *Ikara* A/S missile launcher mounted on the after-deck of the *British Allegiance*.

And the terrible things which happened aboard the Liberian registered death ship *Ayacucho City*. How McReadie and myself had watched the end of the world approaching over the Mediterranean horizon, and how McReadie had lost his scalp . . . But that was another story*, in another sea, and I still didn't want to think about it because it made me go all sick with the fear of what might have happened if J.C. hadn't . . .

J.C. . . . ? Well, he was the man who had started it all. The man who bought, on behalf of the British Government and through various discreetly silent nominees, the entire share-holding of a once destitute shipping company called the British Mutual Steam Navigation Company. And who'd moulded it into the most ruthless, clandestine maritime commando the world has ever known.

Not that the world did know, mind you. Because BMSNC was espionage's most audacious con-trick. And that made Sir James Cromer, VC, KCMG into the world's top con-man, which was quite a mutation from J.C.'s original pre-retirement role.

It indicated that some very unsporting people had been wearing vice-admiral's hats in Her Britannic Majesty's Navy.

*A Plague of Sailors

According to the late commander of the minelayer *Ch'eng Yang* anyway. If he'd known – just before the other twenty-four mines she'd carried had exploded directly beneath his honourable bridge.

In point of fact, I didn't think J.C. was all that much of a sportsman either. Not after McReadie had shoved me into the Old Man's office and I'd stood there waiting to be welcomed back from the dead after the *Ayacucho City* affair, only to hear him say without even looking up from the file on his desk, 'You're an incompetent, Cable! You lost me a good ship when *Commander* went down . . . *and* you damn near started World War Three all on your own!'

I took an involuntary step forward, already aware of a dull, glowing rage. I remembered what I'd screamed at McReadie all that time ago, just before the ship fell over on top of her BMSNC crewmen. About already having been 'Bashed, drowned, melted down into a blob of grease an' run over by half the fuggin' shipping in the fuggin' Med . . .!'

Then I also remembered that it *had* been partly my fault, because I *should* have known about that damned rocket launcher. So I didn't even point out that, incidentally, J.C. had also lost a lot of good blokes as well as a ship.

I just said tightly, 'Yessir!'

And tried to forget the horror of it. All over again.

The little Admiral slammed the file shut and finally consented to look at me. I started to get that uncomfortable feeling – sort of unwanted, almost – which Billy Budd must have experienced while the Master-at-Arms rove the hangman's rope to the measured beat of a pipeclayed Marine drummer. By the time he spoke again I was half expecting it to be from under a black silk headsquare.

'Nothing is achieved without order and discipline, Cable.'

'Sir?'

'Admiral Lord St Vincent. Seventeen ninety eight. D'you recognize the quotation, Cable?'

I shrugged vaguely. Personally I didn't even recognize the bloody admiral and the only St Vincent I knew was a bleak finger of land pointing warningly at your starboard side as you round Portugal, homeward bound.

Another bleak finger pointed at me. Warningly. 'You must be taught discipline, Mister. Which is why you're here . . .'

The corner of my mouth started to twitch. It was a certain indication of my location, just like a DF bearing to a ship at sea, except that my nervous tic invariably manifested itself on, or near, the sixteenth floor of the Company's Head Office in Leadenhall Street, London.

. . . and J.C. was speaking again. Telling me there was only one way a damned irresponsible, ineffectual, uncontrollable moron like me would ever learn the necessity for discipline. And that was – I blinked owlishly at him while he poked a cigar at me with as much feeling as he would have levelled a Sten-gun barrel – 'By imposing it on others, Cable. And by imposing it on yourself, simply because you have no other choice.'

He flicked a lighter and held it out, almost grudgingly. 'That's why I'm giving you *British Venturer*, Cable . . . You'll be in command.'

Of course, I should have known there'd be a snag to it. Like giving a mouse a special piece of cheese – wired to a trap with a spring like something off an elephant's chest expander. But I didn't. I just felt all happy and warm inside.

For a bit.

McReadie watched me dispassionately as I strolled out of J.C.'s office and sat on the edge of his desk. My cigar had gone out, which they always do with me, so I said loftily, 'Light me, Commander.'

'Which foot?' McReadie muttered disinterestedly. 'Left or right?'

'*Captain*.' I murmured deprecatingly.

He swung his legs off the desk. 'I know already, Cable.

I'm the operations bloke in this cut-price navy, or had you forgotten?'

It wasn't quite as satisfying as a common or garden congratulation but McReadie was really only a liaison officer given to BMSNC by MOD Navy anyway, probably because they couldn't find anything else he wasn't too dangerous and homicidally inclined for.

So I just ignored the sour grapes and eyed the still raw purple scar under McReadie's hairline where the Israeli surgeons had sewn the top of his head back down as a permanent legacy to BMSNC's involvement in other people's wars, then said spitefully, 'I see they welded your lid back on, McReadie. Or is it just a toupee stuck down with Sellotape?'

For a moment he glared at me aggressively, then his features softened, slowly crumbling into the old McReadie grin. He came round the desk and punched me gently on the shoulder. 'Let's go see your new ship, huh? Then we'll brief you for the voyage . . . Captain.'

Yet strangely enough, during the next two hours spent down at King George V Dock, while I spent the time poking around *British Venturer* with all the casually concealed pride of a newly appointed master, there was another ship which I couldn't quite forget.

Her name was the *Kuibyshev*.

Because, somehow, I knew that my inexplicable promotion wasn't through merit, but 'expediency'. And that when I stood on *Venturer*'s bridge I was there for a ruthlessly calculated reason. I was going to be an Aunt Sally with a ghost on my shoulder – the ghost of a man called Viktorovich Mikhail Pritytsky.

And they'd shot him. With a frigate!

Venturer was much the same as the majority of the BMSNC fleet, though I must admit that, to my eyes, she was just that little bit sleeker and neater and more ladylike. Mind you, I could have been ever so slightly biased towards her.

Just over ten thousand gross registered tons, she'd been built during the late fifties and, over the next ten years, had churned stolidly round and round the world with her six holds topped up with animal hides and Malayan tin, and motor cars and Scotch whisky and all the million and one articles which appear on a freighter's cargo manifests. And then, gradually, there were too many ships flying too many flags, and the old and disillusioned directors of the British Mutual Steam Navigation Company just couldn't cope any more, so all the ships with the *British* prefix and the Lion Passant house flag spent more and more time in ballast and less and less in employment. Until a fanatical little admiral spoke to a Very Important Person and, lo and behold, the grim old Lion fluttered for a new master, and freight contracts appeared from nowhere to justify the resurrected *British* ships probing into every corner of the globe, even the anti-social ones.

But this time the sailormen were different, and with skills rather more sophisticated than the average voyager's. And the 'accidents' started to happen. And the killing, and the deceit.

And people like me started wondering what McReadie could have meant when he said I was 'expendable', because in BMSNC it covered any possibility from being fired to as good as dead. And I certainly hadn't been fired . . .

The starboard wheelhouse door slid open with a bang and I shocked out of my reverie to see McReadie watching me curiously. Turning away again without speaking I looked out through the high windows, down along the forward well-deck with its open, hungry hatches gaping like the mouths of birds in a nest, waiting for the stuff of their very existence to be proferred by the stork-legged cranes – *Venturer*'s cargo.

My cargo too, now.

McReadie said softly, 'Thinking, Brev? What're you thinking about?'

I let my fingers gently caress the cold brass handles of the telegraph. 'Oh, about . . .!' And I was going to tell him about pride and about love, and about feeling all cosy inside with the warmth that only a seaman can feel about his very own ship. And I knew McReadie would understand because he was a sailorman too and, even more than that, he was my friend despite all the cynicism and knocking.

But I didn't. Because I had a self-imposed image to maintain which didn't allow for the irrelevancies of love and joy and affection. So I just said irritably, '. . . about when the hell someone's going to tell me just what the snag is behind Cable's First Command!'

McReadie watched me unblinkingly. 'There isn't. You're going on a straightforward freighting trip. General cargo with steel scrap in the lower holds.'

He was so utterly sincere and honest about it that I was finally convinced – it guaranteed that he and J.C. were going to sell me down the river. Because, you see, as well as being a friend McReadie was also a patriot. And patriots can tell lies better than any other kind of fanatic, when they believe it's for Queen and Country.

And really solid patriots have a substitute word for all the other, smaller patriots. It was the one which worried me.

That word 'Expendable'.

'Helsinki?' I queried slowly. And very suspiciously. 'You sure you just want me to take her to Helsinki?'

J.C. shifted irritably behind his desk. 'It's in Finland. Starboard side as you go up the Baltic.'

I blinked at McReadie standing behind but he smothered a grin and looked up at the ceiling. Now even the bloody Admiral wanted to be a funny man, which had to be hard for someone with the sense of humour of a cadaver at cremation time. Still, I was determined to find the fly in my particular ointment even if he wore a comic hat and a plastic nose.

'Helsinki,' I echoed to avoid any confusion, 'has absolutely no strategic value whatever. Neither to us nor to Ivan . . has it?'

'Not much,' McReadie said. 'They're a nice, peaceable crowd, the Finns.'

'So why d'you want *British Venturer* up there, then? If we're all mates together?'

'Because we *are* a shipping company, Cable. A large part of our operation is perfectly legitimate deep sea trading. I fail to see why you're being so deliberately obtuse.'

My God, but J.C. looked so terribly sincere and solicitous. It scared the hell out of me, even to see him like that, because I couldn't help but remember another jolly sincere chap who must have given just the same impression despite the few pieces of silver in his burnous. I think his name was Iscariot . . . Judas Iscariot?

I made one last half-hearted effort. 'And can I assume, as I've no ulterior mission, that the ship's clean, then? No torpedo tubes in the tween-deck mountings? Or guns under the deck cargo? Or depth charges or hot electronic gear or infra-red cameras or . . .!'

I stopped suddenly and looked hard at McReadie. Somehow, in some intangible way, I'd detected the slightest trace of discomfort. Maybe it was the look in his eyes. Of sadness, or guilt? Or was it just sympathy? I half opened my mouth to dig a little deeper when J.C. rose abruptly and leaned over the desk.

'Your ship is clean, Cable. Do you understand? *British Venturer* has no secrets . . .' His voice was very low, 'I say again, Captain . . . *No* secrets!'

And by the time I found out just how big a patriotic liar J.C. really was, it was far too late. Because, by then, it was nearly dying time for a few hundred thousand people . . . but that was a lot later.

Turning for the door I said stiffly, 'Very well, sir. If there's nothing else I'll go and prepare my passage plans. London, Helsinki and back . . .'

The little Admiral's voice slashed across my retreat. 'Just

London, Helsinki, Cable. You may not be making the homeward run.'

I halted and, unseen by the two men behind me, closed my eyes tight for a few, frightened seconds. This was more like it! Now this was a *lot* more bloody like it, Cable boyo! This was the BMSNC way of doing things – like don't ever book a return trip because you may never be able to use the ticket.

Or you may come home cheaper. At freight rates. In a wooden box!

And this time McReadie wasn't smiling at all. Not even sardonically. I felt the nervous tic again, tugging at the side of my face, forcing me to take a deep breath before I could even speak at all. 'You jus' said I had no mission. You said the rotten boat was *clean*, f'r . . .'

'*Belay that, Mister!*'

The Admiral's eyes flayed me angrily, bleak as a North Atlantic winter. 'You'll damn well remember just who you are and where you are . . .'

Waves of frustrated, fearful anticipation swamped over me until I wanted to cry, but I didn't. I just clenched my fists tightly and glared defiantly back as he dropped each scathing word into place as neatly as a pattern of depth charges. '. . . and why a man like you is here, Cable – why we're *all* here. Because we're the neutralizers, d'you understand? The alkali to the acid . . .'

I listened without really recording. This was the motivation bit – that a bunch of buccaneering, subversive bastards like us could actually counteract J.C.'s phantom Red Acid. Could really stop it burning and biting and dissolving. The Communist vitriol which was subtly eroding the foundations of every free democracy in the Western World. Oh, it was a great incentive to a new-look John Bull, a real stiff-upper-lip freezer.

Except that I'd heard it all before, a million times before. And I was getting tired now, and cynical. Because the Soviets and the Red Chinese, and the Poles and the East

Germans and the Czechs – they all marched to the same formula. Only with them it was for the Glorious Revolution, and their particular insidious acid was labelled 'Capitalism'.

As far as I was concerned it still meant that, to a Red, Brevet Cable wasn't so much a neutralizer as a bloody target. That made me very unhappy, and scared. Scared as hell.

J.C. slipped into his straight-up, man to man pose. 'When I said you had no mission, Cable, I meant every word of it. Every word.'

I blinked out of my philosophical limbo. 'Yessir. So may I ask just what you did have in mind when you inferred a one-way Baltic cruise? I mean, why shouldn't I bring *Venturer* back after clearing Helsinki?'

He chewed his lip thoughtfully, grey eyes probing deeply into mine, then he swung round to the huge northern hemisphere chart on the wall behind him. 'I think, first, Captain, you should appreciate the background. The setting for your next voyage.

'Anglo-Soviet relations,' he continued heavily, 'have for some considerable time now been suffering a steadily increasing strain.'

And no bloody wonder, I reflected moodily, with squires like him trampling all over the faces of the proletarian workers – like me. Then I remembered I was a four ringer, a ship's captain too now, so I could always grind a few faces here and there myself, and I started feeling a little glimmer of consolation. Anyway, come to that the best peasant grinders in the business come out of that Red Acid bottle – those comrades with a few bars on their shoulders who argue that the best way of governing your brother is with a tank. Aiming straight at him.

The senior decadent bourgeois across the desk continued, 'Twelve days ago the International situation escalated into a new and more serious phase, Cable – from passive irritation to open, physical interference . . . the Soviets illegally detained and searched one of our ships.'

31

' "Ours" meaning BMSNC?' I queried, still trying to be as unco-operative as I dared.

McReadie stepped in, smoothly diplomatic. ' "Ours", meaning British . . . Ship called the *Pentland Firth*, bound for Iceland. Her Old Man did everything but throw the bloody anchor at 'em but they still carried on going through his papers and manifests with a fine-tooth comb.'

I frowned. 'They must have had a reason?'

'Oh, they did, Cable!' J.C. snorted, 'And it's one we've seen coming since the early fifties – they've been reading their history books. They've learned fast that sea power is still one of the major keys to world domination. Dammit, we British even wrote the book. The Royal Navy's proved it over the past several hundred years. And now the *Pentland Firth* affair shows that the Reds are ready to go that little bit further – to experimentally flex their maritime muscles, you might say.'

McReadie nodded. 'And another point. The sea is international, boundaries are much more obscure and undefined. There's room for jostling without whole-hearted committal . . . On land, if a soldier steps across a border then he's an aggressor. There's no way of saving face other than to mobilize and shoot the poor sod. And all his mates. Then tomorrow it's war, an' the next day it's nuclear . . .'

'Whereas with the *Pentland Firth* they left room for manoeuvre?' I said. 'They were just testing our reactions before they went any deeper?'

'And, by God but they got them!' J.C. growled.

I glanced at McReadie. 'The Kooby-whatsit?'

'*Kuibyshev*. Just like I told you earlier . . . except our crowd went a little over-enthusiastic and shot her Old Man right off his own bridge. It's made the Kremlin a bit angry.'

Which, I thought, could have been classed as the understatement of the decade. I could sense we were rapidly approaching the crunch, though. I already knew our policy was only intended to have been of a tit-for-tat nature. If the Reds buzzed one of our ships, then we buzz one of theirs.

If they crowded us, then we jostle them . . . but no further. No escalation from the British side. Just a 'Hands Off or else' warning.

A cynic might have added, 'Or else what?' but I was too anxious to find out where Captain Cable and the good ship *British Venturer* came into this little Anglo-Soviet game of thermo-nuclear chess. And I had a nasty premonition it was to be in the super-heated rising bit, the one in the middle of the mushroom.

But, like I said earlier, J.C. was such a sincere liar that it never got beyond a premonition.

Not right then, anyway.

Intuition made me stare hard from McReadie to the Admiral. 'But now the Soviets have made another move, haven't they? In retaliation for the *Kuibyshev*?'

J.C. snapped shortly, 'Yes.'

I nodded. 'Which is why I'm to take *Venturer* to Helsinki. Right . . . *Sir*?' Jeeeeze, but it was like trying to borrow heroin from a junkie.

McReadie stepped forward holding a long white cylinder. He unrolled it beside the desk and I saw it was a navigator's chart. I moved over beside him, despite my now fatalistic acceptance I still couldn't help gazing curiously to see what the future held for me, all laid out on the snowy mariner's crystal before me.

Admiralty Chart Number 2816, Baltic Sea, Southern Sheet.

He tapped a point just inside the western end of the Baltic, in the sea area bounded by Sweden, Denmark and Germany. 'Two days ago Whitehall received a formal note of protest over the *Kuibyshev* incident from the USSR.'

I shrugged. 'So why are we looking at the Baltic? That other shambles occurred in the Norwegian Sea.'

McReadie tapped again. 'The same note also contained a statement, issued on the authority of the Presidium of the Supreme Soviet. It was a short, unequivocal directive . . .'

He looked at me dispassionately. '. . . it stated that, as

from midnight on the seventeenth of this month, the area of the Baltic Sea east of thirteen degrees east will be declared closed to all British shipping. And that all Soviet Fleet Units have been directed to ensure that this blockade be effected by using any means at their disposal.'

I started to feel the hairs on the back of my neck rising, but I still had that damned image to live up to. I blinked at the impassive faces before me and grinned uncertainly. 'Christ!' I said, hopefully, 'But they can't do that. I mean, well, they *can't* just lower the boom on the first ship that goes in, dammit!'

J.C.'s voice was deceptively mild. 'We say that too, Cable. Which means that — as yours *will* be the first vessel through the closed area — we shall prove ourselves absolutely right by defying them with impunity.'

He smiled wintrily, then shrugged. 'Or, of course, wrong . . . when the Russians sink you!'

Two

And we got nearly fourteen miles past the meridian of thirteen degrees east before they did.

Try to sink us, I mean.

Only a few minutes earlier I'd been in the chartroom watching while Mike Ritchie, my Chief Officer, transferred the latest set of bearings on to our previously laid off course line. He worked quickly and neatly and I thought gloomily how nice it would have been still to be a first mate like him, instead of feeling the tensions of command closing around me like a hangman's rope.

He looked up and the dim light from the Angle-Poise picked out a carefree, resolute mouth under a pair of brown, boyish eyes. 'We'll be abeam of Kap Arkona in nine minutes, sir. Then we alter to pass south of the Adlergrund.'

Moving over to the table beside him I nodded. This was the bit I didn't like. The part of the passage where we deliberately veered south, towards the East German coast, instead of taking the more direct route up through Swedish waters via the Bornholmsgat. I reflected savagely on how J.C. had insisted that we not only defied the Soviet threat but we also got cheeky doing it. It was like a fly knocking on the trapdoor spider's lid as it strolled past.

Then giving him a soldier's farewell when he looked out!

Cramming my cap on the back of my head I stepped out across the coaming to the port bridge wing, dimly shadowed by the grey dawn light. 'Make damn sure we split that thirteen fathom mark north of the Oder, Mister Ritchie,' I threw over my shoulder, 'I want plenty of sea room rounding the tail of the Rönne Bank. Just in case.'

I walked out to the end of the wing and stared nervously

down at the red glow washing from the port sidelight. Just in case of what, Cable boy? Just in case we had to run away from a *Komar* Class fast patrol boat that could do three knots to every one of ours *and* launch its two *Styx* missiles before I could even get from where I stood to the cardboard shelter of *Venturer*'s wheelhouse . . .? Or maybe they'd let their airmen nibble a bit of the cake instead, and punch us vertically into the Baltic under a strike from a TU-16 bomber-launched *Kennel* anti-ship rocket?

I turned to face aft, back to where the flat, featureless topography of Denmark had faded into the horizon. It was a clear night, with the apparently crazy, undisciplined sparks of the buoys homing on Copenhagen Sound blinking gaily into the crisp, coming dawn. I wondered if we'd ever see them again, if we'd ever get the chance to round Krieger's Flak homeward bound, with the jackstaff of *Venturer*'s bow shouldering the welcoming flash from the Falsterborev Lightship.

My hand brushed the sanded teak rail as I swung forward again and I let it rest there a moment, feeling the steady throb of the engines transmitted up through the frames of the ship. It felt good to me, like the pulse of a healthy athlete to a surgeon, and just for a few fleeting seconds my mind went back quite a lot of years to when, as a very young cadet, I'd held on to the rails of my first ship and closed my eyes and pretended she was mine. Just for a few, fairy-tale seconds . . .

A movement beside me broke the magic. 'Second Mate has a contact, sir. On radar.'

I saw it was the Fourth Mate, Timson. 'Whereaway, Mister Timson?'

'Broad on the starboard bow, sir. Extreme range at the moment.'

'Thank you. Let me know as soon as he has her estimated course and speed.'

He moved back into the wheelhouse and I leant on the rail, staring thoughtfully into the darkness ahead. It didn't really mean anything yet, one remote radar echo. There were a lot of ships in the Baltic Sea and no one so far had come up with a way of distinguishing types. Or of recognizing the difference between those with guns and those without. Or of picking out the different nationalities. I grinned cynically – if they ever did, then no doubt the Soviets would insist on a nice revolutionary red blip for themselves. And the British? Why, dammit, sir – Red, white and blue! What else?

A match flared briefly in the lee of the chartroom. Mike Ritchie allowing himself the luxury of an early morning cigarette. I didn't turn round because I didn't really want to talk to anybody right then, I just wanted to be able to think, to sink back into the escapist past again, and imagine what things might have been like if only I'd never met McReadie all those years ago. McReadie with the winning blarney of an Irish Recruiting Sergeant and the scruples of the Spithead Press.

And, talking about press gangs, there was that other chip on my shoulder – the one with the initials J.C.

The one who'd said, so casually that he might have been asking me to post a letter for him, 'And incidentally, Captain, if the Reds *do* order you to stop your ship, please remember I am sending *Venturer* in to test their determination. We must learn exactly how far the Soviet Government intend to go . . . Personally I think they'll retract. They were forced to back down over the Cuban issue, remember?'

I'd muttered 'Yessir,' with all the enthusiasm of a blind eunuch anticipating a striptease display, then he'd continued slowly and emphatically, 'Which is why, Captain, you will *not* heave to when challenged. D'you understand me, Cable? You will maintain your standard course and speed for as long as humanly possible. And right up to the time when you are actually fired upon.'

To which I'd replied, in quasi-debonair jollity, that I sincerely hoped the Red gunners would be a bit more bloody expert at putting shots across other people's bows than a certain naval frigate I knew.

And *he'd* retorted, without any jollity whatsoever, 'I'm not talking about shots across your bows, man. I say again, Cable – You are specifically ordered not to take action to stop your ship, despite any coercion they may apply. Not until they have fired upon . . . and actually *hit* . . . *British Venturer.*'

Which, if it still didn't convince the British Government of exactly how far Ivan was prepared to toss the ball, was going to be one helluva proof positive for Brevet Cable.

While I bobbed around the Baltic up to my ears in a life-jacket.

If I had a head left for my ears to stick on to.

Hell, they hadn't even given me a Third Officer, probably to avoid unnecessary waste . . .

Someone came up behind me and I sensed the glowing tip of a cigarette suspended in the darkness. Mike Ritchie's voice sounded quiet. 'D'you think they'll really use force to stop us, sir? Now we're calling their bluff?'

I nearly rounded on him in savage frustration, yelling that *I* was bloody wondering *that* much myself, but I didn't. Because I suddenly remembered that he was a volunteer for this operation. That he'd actually offered his neck to be laid on the block to defy the Red chopper. And not only Mike Ritchie but all the rest of *Venturer*'s crewmen. Except me, of course – Captain bloody Courageous.

So I only shrugged and tried to sound dourly phlegmatic. 'If they do, Mister Ritchie, then I trust we shall be as efficient at abandoning ship as we are at abandoning the dictates of common sense.'

Which – apart from letting him know I was a pretty cool commander – also showed him I wasn't just a puppet who jerked on J.C.'s strings without even a word of criticism. Which I secretly was. But that was Cable's image once more, always needing a boost.

Then the Fourth Mate came out of the wheelhouse again and this time he sounded a lot more tense than I would have liked. 'Second Mate says could you glance at the radar, sir? We now have three contacts converging which . . . well, appear to be in formation. In line ahead, sir.'

I forced myself to stay at a walk as far as the Decca console. Somehow I knew that this was it, what we'd been expecting from the minute we crossed that invisible meridian of thirteen degrees east. So now all we had to do was wait a little longer and we'd find out at first hand just who was right. Just wait like a row of bottles in a shooting gallery . . . or like puppets.

The amber glow washed the Second Mate's features with a luminous Costa Del Sol tinge. He looked up as I approached and stepped back smartly, gesturing at the set. 'Three ships, Captain. All much the same size and definitely in line ahead . . . I'd say they were on an interception course with us, probably homing on our radar transmission.'

Mike Ritchie called, 'Arkona's coming abeam now, sir. Shall I alter to the new heading still?'

I bit my lip thoughtfully. If the unidentified blips *were* out to intercept and investigate us then they would also have to alter in relation to our new course. Which meant we'd know for sure . . . I kept my voice level. 'Please do, Mister Ritchie. You have the watch.'

He moved over to stand beside the quartermaster at the wheel and I heard him say, 'Starboard ten the wheel, steady on one one five '

The ship lay fractionally over to port as the helmsman put the wheel down, giving us ten degrees of rudder. His head cocked slightly to one side like an attentive seagull's as he watched the clicking gyro card tick through its controlled arc. Then expert hands released the wheel and the ship came upright again on her new heading.

'Steady on one one five, sir.'

'Thank you.'

I bent over the radar console and pressed my forehead into the soft foam rubber cup of the reflector hood. Behind me, Twist, the Second Mate, murmured, 'The targets bear

39

roughly green two oh relative, sir.'

I had to smile even though it wasn't funny. I knew he was only using the correct formula, but – targets? It was like a scuttling mouse thinking of the three predatory pussies on his tail as the 'prey'.

Blinking a few times to get used to the optical demands of the translucent screen I quickly picked out the brighter horizontal switchback that was the coast of Rügen, then, further to the right, a break in the line which must have been the entrance into the Greifswalder Bodden and, almost at the top of the circle, the continuing coastline of East Germany proper.

And, precisely midway between the land trace and the centre of the screen, which was us, there were three distinct, elongated blips. All in a straight line, and all arrowing to a meeting point a few miles ahead of *British Venturer*.

I spun the ranging knob gently, watching as the bright, wriggly worm of light expanded towards the contacts, rejuvenated every few seconds by the continuous rotation of the scanner. Waiting until the range ring bisected the first of the ghost ships I glanced up at the distance scale.

'Twenty-seven and a half miles, Mister Twist.' I said, straightening up and glancing at the watching Second Mate, 'Assuming they are intending to intercept, perhaps you would be good enough to estimate their speed of advance and calculate what time we should expect to raise them visually. Mister Timson can stay on the Decca.'

I stepped out on the bridge wing again, aware of the helmsman's eyes fixed enquiringly on my back. It gave me a funny feeling because, while I'd seen a lot of actions before, up to now I'd always been one of the followers myself, one of the people who just did what they were told without having to worry whether or not they were doing the right thing.

Maybe being a puppet wasn't all bad, at that. And the hell with the rugged individualist image.

The Mate came out of the wheelhouse and leant over the

rail beside me. It was rapidly becoming lighter now and I could see the fair ends of hair protruding from under his cap band, ruffling in the seventeen knot breeze over the dodgers. He looked at his watch. 'I've sent all hands down for an early breakfast, sir. The Chief's going to arrange reliefs for engine-room watchkeepers . . .' He grinned uncertainly. '. . . the crowd we've got aboard'll face the whole Red Navy so long as they've got full bellies.'

I nearly said they maybe wouldn't float so damn good though, but I sort of hoped we weren't going to get shot at by the *whole* of the Russian Baltic Fleet myself, so I just scrubbed reflectively at the bristles on my chin and said gruffly, 'I'm going below for a shave, Mister Ritchie. Will you please have coffee brought up to the bridge for when I return.'

I turned towards the bridge ladder thinking that, even if I wasn't exactly J.C.'s favourite captain, at least I was going to be the smartest survivor in the Baltic. Or the neatest, nicest-smelling cadaver.

At the top of the ladder I hesitated briefly. Twist came tumbling out of the chartroom cramming his cap on the back of his head as he did so but, when he saw me watching, he sort of skidded to a halt and converted it to the more leisurely, dignified approach of a ship's officer before his Master Mariner.

I knew what he was going to say before he even spoke. It was all there in the mixture of excitement and apprehension on his young face. 'They *have* altered to a new intercept course, sir . . .'

It was my big chance. The new image of an unruffled, iron-nerved Cable who stared crisis in the face and hardly spared it a thought. So I just raised a negligent eyebrow and said quietly, '*They*, Mister Twist?'

He blinked. 'The *Russians*, sir. The three contacts.'

'Ah. Then if we assume, for the moment, that you are correct in your assumption . . .' That didn't sound quite right. '. . . perhaps you would be good enough to inform me of when we can expect to sight, and positively identify them?'

God, but I was a cool bastard.

He gazed at me in positive hero worship. 'In approximately twenty minutes, sir. At 06.40.'

I nodded laconically. 'Thank you, Mister Twist. Then I still have nineteen minutes in which to shave.'

I was nearly half-way down the ladder, congratulating myself on having made at least one disciple that day, before I caught Twist's rather penetrating voice talking to the Fourth Mate from the wheelhouse.

He giggled, 'No kiddin', Four Oh. The Old Man's thick as last week's gravy – he'd even forgotten those contacts are Ivans. And imagine needing nineteen minutes to *shave*, f'r Chrissake . . .'

It actually took me four minutes for that shave, plus another three to change into a clean shirt. The other twelve I spent prowling up and down in my day-room, staring at an apparently immobile clock and wishing to God I'd been a farmer instead of a sailorman. It was the period when time stood still for me, and it cured me forever of making bloody silly attempts to be remembered as one of the great casual quoters of the twentieth century.

I hit the top step of the port bridge ladder at precisely 06.39 hours.

It was full daylight now, with the ship whispering along through an almost flat calm. Even under the pervading atmosphere of tension I still noticed how nice she looked with the bright varnished teak panels glowing warmly and all the white paintwork reflecting a rose-tinted sunrise. But even that had a snag to it – that same lovely sun kiss had already washed the spires of the Kremlin, and the hills and valleys and Steppes of the distant USSR . . . it made it all seem a bit second-hand, somehow. And threatening.

The Chief and Second Mates were out on the starboard wing, hanging over the fore end with binoculars glued to their eyes, both scanning the horizon fine on our starboard bow for the first sign of masts breaking the earth's curvature. Mike Ritchie straightened up as I walked through the wheelhouse and came up behind him.

'Your coffee's in the chartroom, sir. And the contacts are still closing for an intercept. The masthead lookout had already raised them but they're too far off to identify.'

I glanced up at the foretopmast, up above the huge blocks of the jumbo derrick to where the seaman hung over the rim of the drum-shaped crow's nest. Even as I watched he reached down and picked up his telephone while, at the same time, the bridge set buzzed urgently. Mike Ritchie snatched the receiver off its cradle just fast enough to betray the anxiety we all felt but wouldn't admit.

'Bridge!'

He listened for a few moments, then said 'Thank you,' and came back out to me. 'They're confirmed as warships, sir. Conventional tripod masts, the lot.'

I noticed young Twist eyeing me covertly while still pretending to sweep the sea ahead. It brought that strange, helpless feeling back again. That sense of overwhelming responsibility in that, out of all the men aboard *British Venturer*, I was the only one who couldn't depend on a higher authority to do my thinking for me. I suddenly realized what J.C. had meant that time – when he said command was the one thing to teach me self-discipline – because now I had no other choice. No one to pass the decisions over to.

And in less than half an hour I was going to have to make decisions which, if taken at the wrong time or in the wrong way, could litter this sun-dappled sea with a threshing carpet of dying men screaming from their bier of choking fuel oil. Screaming at *me*, f'r Chrissakes! At me, Brevet Cable . . . Screaming out of imploding lungs and fear-black, contorted faces . . .

. . . *If* the Soviets even gave me the chance to decide anything in the first place.

I said laconically, 'Thank you, Mister Ritchie. Continue

43

our present course and speed. I shall be in the chartroom if you want me.'

And it wasn't until I was safely in the hidden privacy of the little cabin that I dared to close my eyes and grip the edge of the chart table to fight down the acrid sickness of fear.

I managed one cup of black, tasteless coffee before the Mate knocked deferentially. 'We have them in sight from the bridge now, sir. All three of them.'

He half turned away, then hesitated. 'I've ordered the outboard gripes to be unshipped from the lifeboats. And the securing straps from the Beaufort rafts. Just in case.'

There was that phrase again – just in case. I wondered if Whitehall were also taking any measures to prepare for what might happen if those three ships out there really intended to back political manoeuvring by force of arms. Like activate their local government underground centres, or belatedly try to breath life back into a bureaucratically assassinated Civil Defence Force . . . Just in case.

'Make sure everybody has their lifejacket close by, Mister.'

I stepped out into the bright sunlight and involuntarily looked ahead, out past Second Officer Twist's hunched shoulders as he leaned over the rail, out to where the long low shapes of the warships angled towards us. 'And have both radio officers stand by in the WT Room right away.'

Ritchie asked, 'D'you want to make a "Contact" signal? Let the Company know the action's about to start?'

I glanced at him and smiled deprecatingly. 'Whatever for, Mister Ritchie? We're an ordinary merchantman about our legal business. As yet we have no reason whatsoever to suspect that those warships intend any move other than the appropriate exchange of courtesies. Normality, that's our motto for today . . . and let's save the outraged scream of bloody indignation for when it's justified.'

Which should be any time now, give or take a few eternities.

The Fourth Mate stood behind Twist with an open ship

ID book in his hands. The Second murmured slowly, peering through his Barr and Strouds, 'Destroyer type. Two funnels raked aft . . . One fore-deck main armament, twin turret, and . . . yeah. Same again on after-deck. Two banks torpedo tubes port side, probably same to starboard . . . an' twin tripod masts with director turret abaft the bridge . . . Check.'

'Check, Mate.' The Fourth leafed through the pages then tapped the book positively. 'Got the bast . . .'

He saw me watching and looked confused for a moment, then his face cleared. 'I think they're *Skory* . Class, sir. Fleet destroyers.'

I raised an eyebrow. 'Russian, Laotian or Martian, Mister Timson?'

He said, solemnly dead-pan, 'Oh, Soviet, sir. Definitely Soviet . . . Thirty-six knots, four 5.1-inch, two 3-inch plus AA batteries. And torpedo tubes, of course. Five tube broadside . . .' He consulted the book again with academic interest, '. . . Built around nineteen fifty-six, complement of two-sixty crewmen. Oh, and three an' a half thousand tons displ . . .'

I said abruptly, '*Thank* you, Mister Timson. I am familiar with the type.'

While it was nice to think my officers were still capable of professional detachment at a time like this, I also preferred not to think too hard about the opposition's capacity for dispensing sudden death by remote control. And anyway, come to that, if they'd been three rowing boats with cata-pults they'd still have been armed a damn sight more effectively than us aboard this maritime clay pigeon.

Mike Ritchie murmured quietly, 'Looks like It then.'

I raised my binoculars and uneasily inspected the leading destroyer, thinking how evil and rapacious she looked with the long raked stem shearing a high white fan of a bow wave from the sparkling sea under her forefoot.

'Indeed it does, Mister Ritchie.' I lowered the glasses and chewed my lip thoughtfully, 'Indeed it does.'

Then a signal lamp commenced to stutter from the flotilla leader's bridge, and the king-sized guessing game had started.

The funny thing about it was that I stopped feeling scared the very minute that first Soviet destroyer called us up so peremptorily. All of a sudden I realized just what a certain Captain Viktorovich Mikhail Pritytsky must have felt when *he* was pushed around in the Norwegian Sea by a bloody obnoxious frigate. In fact the only real difference between him and I was that he hated the White Ensign almost as much as I detested the Colours those three pirates were steaming under.

So I started to get mad. Curiously, uncharacteristically mad.

And from then on I didn't need orders from any angry little admirals in Whitehall to get all bloody-minded and stubborn either. Not any more.

'They're calling us, sir,' Ritchie said unnecessarily. 'Do you intend to ignore them?'

I shook my head. 'Acknowledge. We'll see what they have to say first. Perhaps they want to wish us God speed and Bon Voyage, eh Mister Twist?'

The Second Mate grinned in a pleased sort of way and everyone else tittered dutifully. 'Or maybe they want to surrender to us, sir.'

Then the Aldis clattered sharply in the Fourth Mate's hands . . . TTTTTTTT . . . and all eyes fastened on to the Russian, waiting the next move. It came almost immediately.

It was short, emphatic, and to the point. They didn't even bother with the International Code, just a plain language signal in English. STOP YOUR SHIP . . . PREPARE TO RECEIVE BOARDING PARTY.

For a moment I wondered how they'd known so quickly that we were qualified game for the Red Navy shooting season, then I remembered that with a name like *British*

46

Venturer plastered all over the length of our bows they could hardly mistake us for a Chinese junk. Still, it was full daylight now and there was hardly any point in being coy about our pedigree.

'Mister Timson.'

'Sir?'

'Be good enough to have the stand-by quartermaster hoist the Red Ensign, if you would.'

'Aye, aye, sir.' He turned away, rather regretfully I thought, and disappeared into the wheelhouse after handing the Aldis over to Twist. The Second Mate glanced at me queryingly. 'Do I acknowledge their signal, sir?'

I tried to look relaxed. 'Send, IT IS NOT CONVENIENT TO EXERCISE SIGNALS.'

Crease lines appeared faintly round Mike Ritchie's mouth. 'Playing dumb, then?'

I smiled fractionally too. Playing dumb had to be a pretty easy thing for me to do or I wouldn't have been here in the first place. Or was that just Cable being toughly cynical again? It didn't matter all that much anyway, not now we were past the point of no return, so I murmured, 'Not dumb, Mister Ritchie. Just awkward.'

The Aldis chattered behind us as we watched the three grey, immaculately-spaced ships sweep die-straight down our starboard side, each pushing a bleached white bow wave ahead of her and each precisely five cables off. A curt sparkle of light from the lead destroyer's bridge punctuated every word sent by Twist, confirming that they'd received – if not exactly appreciated – our obtuse retort.

The Mate said objectively, 'They're pretty sure of themselves. All batteries still trained fore and aft . . . Trusting bastards.'

I didn't answer but I knew what he meant. I'd also noticed how they'd left themselves wide open to attack because it had obviously never occurred to them that we were anything other than what we appeared to be – a stolidly plodding, inoffensive British ploughshare. I wondered, with the somewhat homicidal detachment of a BMSNC-orientated buccaneer, just how trusting those proletarian Jolly Jack Tars would have remained if their three sitting ducks had kept right on going, still in perfect line ahead and at thirty knots, but right down to the bottom of the Baltic – with their double bottoms eviscerated by a fan of twenty-one-inch torpedoes spat from concealed mountings in *Venturer*'s tween-decks.

Except that we didn't *have* any illicit weaponry this trip out. Because our old lion's teeth had been drawn, emasculating us to the status of an expendable international incident, an ocean-going sacrificial cow. A disposable instrument to measure the strength of determination behind the threat.

I knew all that because J.C. had said so.

Well he *did*. Didn't he?

Twist lowered the Aldis and said quickly, 'They're breaking formation, sir.'

There wasn't much we could do other than swallow our frustration and just watch while the host fleet took up their positions for the reception. They looked damnably efficient too, as the first pair of destroyers suddenly swung over, curving round in a tight sweep to port with the white water boiling angrily under grey counters, while the third ship expressed across our stern, smashing contemptuously through our subsiding wake towards our own port quarter.

Until, having reached a point well astern of us like the upper serifs of a Roman 'Y', they simultaneously went into a skidding, skating about-turn through a precise 135 degree arc which must have left the unwary with still travelling stomachs, then came streaking back up abeam of *Venturer* with an easy grace that made me hate show-offs.

'Clever sods,' the Mate gritted, which proved he was just as jealous as me.

Then the flaring bows of the warships dropped as one and they reduced speed with an almost tangible condescension, to take up station on either side of us, leaving a one thousand yard gap between.

The gladiators were in position. All it needed now was the whistle to start the final round.

And that came, too. An anticipatory thirty seconds later.

The flotilla leader's signal lamp seemed very bright this time . . . HEAVE TO STOP THIS IS NOT AN EXERCISE STOP I INTEND TO BOARD YOU END OF MESSAGE.

I couldn't pretend to misunderstand that, not even if I'd been the densest kind of master with a bowler hat, clay pipe and bloody bulldog. Swinging round to Ritchie I snapped, 'Now you *can* act the injured innocent, Mister. Instruct Sparks to send out an "All Ships" call. Plain language RT . . . Say, "*MV British Venturer* under illegal instructions to heave to from unidentified foreign warships. Please send assistance." Then include our position . . . Got that?'

'Sir.'

He shot into the wheelhouse, reaching for the phone. Ritchie knew as well as I did that we were all on our own in this but the call for help had the right sort of bewildered appeal about it that the Soviets would expect. The 'unidentified' bit was only a childish inclusion on my part, like a kiddie spitting futilely in the school playground.

They must have taken it to heart, though – there's nothing which affronts a navy's dignity more than the victim petulantly complaining that it doesn't even know *which* bloody navy's waving the big stick. The minute the Reds started picking up our transmission their bridge lamp twinkled irritably again. AUTHORITY SOVIET FEDERAL STATES STOP HEAVE TO IMMEDIATELY YOU ARE IN PROHIBITED AREA STOP.

I gestured grimly to Twist. 'Reply, THIS IS BRITISH REPEAT BRITISH SHIP STOP I MUST REFUSE TO COMPLY YOUR REQUEST STOP FURTHER QUERY YOUR AUTHORITY, END OF MESSAGE.'

Ritchie came back out to the wing and stood beside me, balancing easily to the slow roll of the ship. He looked anxiously over towards the silently escorting port destroyer. 'We're coming abeam of the Adlergrund now, sir. Nearly time to alter nor'east, up towards Bornholm . . . Except that it'll mean cutting sharp across the bows of Ivan Three back there.'

I chewed my lip. Any alteration of course right now could be misconstrued by the opposition – even taken as a God-sent justification to escalate the incident – yet, on the other hand, if we stayed on our present heading we'd shortly be in East German waters proper, and that was like putting our heads on the executioner's block then giving him a chopper for Christmas . . .

The Second Mate called abruptly, 'They're bringing their turrets to bear at last, sir. An' the lead boat's signalling again.'

I was uncomfortably aware of my belly muscles constricting as I whipped the Barr and Strouds up to my eyes in time to see – instead of an elongated profile – the stubby, face-to-face view of a Russian man o' war's forward gun shield, with a neat little black dot on either side to show where the bangs came from.

And it followed automatically that, if I could see down the barrels, then I was also standing right where the bloody bangs went *to*!

Young Timson clambered up the starboard ladder from the boat-deck and I glanced aft over his shoulder to where the Red Ensign now fluttered colourfully from our own poop. I said sharply, 'Get back down again and take charge of the deck, Mister. I want every man who isn't on watch out of sight and behind cover, probably over on the port side. That means no audience, d'you understand?'

The Fourth Mate threw one startled glance over to the Soviet ships, saw the silent menace aiming straight at him, yelled 'Aye, aye, sir . . .' over his shoulder, and tumbled back down the ladder with barely suppressed excitement. Watching him go I remembered cynically that this was his first trip as a BMSNC hatchet man and hoped to God his patriotic ardour wasn't shortly going to be dampened somewhat as his shipmates around him were reduced to anonymous little bits and pieces of men under the super-heated blast of an exploding shell.

And then – suddenly – everything seemed to happen at once.

Twist said flatly, 'Message reads, STOP YOUR ENGINES IMMEDIATELY OR I WILL OPEN FIRE ON YOU . . . That's all, sir.'

While Mike Ritchie stuck his head out of the wheelhouse, glanced at the bulkhead clock, and called, 'Clear of the Rönne Bank now, Captain. Should be coming round to oh four five in two minute . . .'

But he never did finish the sentence, and we never altered course to head for the Island of Bornholm.

Because that was the moment when the impatient captain of a Soviet destroyer in the Baltic Sea said, 'Fire!'

In Russian, of course.

Three

It was an odd reaction but, just for a split second, I thought someone had torn a piece of heavy canvas. I'd even swung half-way round with the first flush of temper stinging my cheeks to find out which silly bastard was playing games with my already whip-taut nervous system.

Then the shell landed, and I pivoted the other way to face forward again, aware for the moment that my mouth had dropped open but too surprised to close it.

Strangely enough, during the seconds of time it took for that column of amber water to climb incredibly into the sky ahead of our bows, all I could think of was, 'That's funny, Cable boy, but I could've sworn they wouldn't use live round f'r openers. Not *live* go-off-with-a-bloody-bang shells, they wouldn't . . .'

But they did. And by the time that atomized water had reached its zenith we were steaming through the centre of it, with the spray collapsing back across our fo'c'slehead in an admonishing rainbow and the fine, windborne particles blowing aft over the bridge itself so that the acrid taste and smell of cordite prickled our senses.

Tentatively the Mate left off trying to squeeze the teak rail in half and grimaced bitterly. 'Damn good shooting, that. Couldn't've landed more than fifty yards ahead of our stem . . .'

I just hoped to God it wasn't bad shooting instead, and that it had been meant to hit us fifty yards *abaft* the stem, but it was a little late for conjecture. Pushing roughly past him I dived into the wheelhouse, clawing for the WT Room phone. Stabbing the call button I threw over my shoulder at the helmsman, 'Steady as she goes, Burroughs . . . Set her on auto-pilot but stand by the wheel.'

Then the Senior Operator's voice answered remotely, with only a suspicion of excitement. 'Wireless room.'

'Captain here. Transmit on twenty-one, eighty-two Kiloherz . . . MAYDAY MAYDAY MAYDAY THIS IS BRITISH VENTURE MY POSITION IS . . .' I made a quick calculation in my head, not caring much whether I was right or not because I knew that no one could risk escalating this particular Anglo-Soviet fracas to international proportions anyway, '. . . POSITION IS TWO THUREE MILES EAST BY NORTH KOL-LICKERORT LIGHT AM BEIN . . .'

Ritchie's head came through the wheelhouse door. 'Destroyer's flashing again, sir. D'you want to acknowledge?'

I finished urgently, '. . . AM BEING FIRED ON BY SOVIET FLEET UNIT PLEASE STAND BY THIS CHANNEL . . . Got that, Sparks?' then slammed back out on to the spray-dappled bridge, eyes probing for the grey ship across the water.

The Cyclopean eye of her signal lamp blinked a final group then fell blank. Second Mate Twist followed up quickly, 'Message reads – HEAVE TO BRITISH VENTURER REPEAT HEAVE TO IMMEDIATELY . . . I INTEND TO OPEN FIRE ON YOUR SHIP IN TWO MINUTES IF NEGATIVE ACTION TAKEN END OF MESSAGE.'

Mike Ritchie said, almost distantly, 'It's going to be a long, long two minutes. Bloody long.'

Personally I thought it was half a lifetime too short, but I knew what he meant. My legs started to go all shaky with the delayed reaction to the shot of a few moments earlier, or maybe it was with the realization that Cable's moment of truth finally had arrived, just like J.C. said it would, and now that it had happened I wondered if I was going to have the guts to stay away from those bright brass engine-room telegraphs and – at the same time – maybe kill a lot of sailormen because I did.

If I had the guts? To do nothing? To take 'Negative Action', just like the man aboard the can said . . .? It was certainly easier than being a hero, was doing nothing, especially when you're *ordered* to do nothing. I mean, you can't order a hero to be heroic, can you? But, then again, if he only does what he is ordered, then he's not a proper hero anyway . . . Which meant that I could be flailing the Baltic within two minutes, with a hole in the top of my skull and a gallon of dieso fuel corroding my lungs, yet I still wouldn't even be a bloody *hero*, f'r Chrissakes . . .!

The bulkhead clock said ninety seconds to shrapnel time.

I whirled abruptly to see Ritchie and Twist watching expectantly. Above their heads I was conscious of the high bulk of the funnel rolling lazily against the blue morning sky, only the faintest haze of exhaust fumes puttering steadily aft to show we were still at passage speed. That and the evenly transmitted vibration of our engines through the caulked wooden bridge-deck. Defiant, stubbornly continuing vibrations.

'Mister Ritchie. Get down aft and muster your damage control party under the break of the centrecastle. Don't run any hose lines yet, they're probably less open to splinter damage as they are . . . Mister Twist?'

'Sir.'

'Try those bas . . . Try the Russian with the lamp again and make damn sure you log the signal texts after. Say again BRITISH REPEAT BRITISH SHIP IN INTERNATIONAL WATERS . . . YOUR REQUEST IS ILLEGAL . . . AM AWAITING OWNER'S INSTRUCTIONS, end of message.'

I caught sight of Mike Ritchie out of the corner of my eye. He was still standing waiting and his young face looked aggressively tight. A surreptitious glance at the clock – one minute left! Christ! I jerked my chin angrily, 'You should be aft, Mister. Please be good enough to . . .'

He interrupted brusquely, 'You think they're going to hit the bridge first, don't you? So why can't you let Twist take damage control an' I'll take the wheel . . . send Burroughs below as well.'

I smashed my hand down on the bridge rail in an over-whelming blaze of temper. All I needed right now was a bloody boy scout Gunga Din instead of a competent executive officer. 'I said, get *aft*, Mister! I don't know if they'll even have the guts to open fire at all but, by God, if they do then I don't intend to have both senior deck officers condensed within the range of one shell blast . . .'

The Second Mate called urgently, 'Sorry sir, but they won't acknowledge my call. Just keep sending STOP STOP STOP, all the bloody time.'

It brought me up with a round turn. Feeling the anger drain away in a welter of hopelessness I said dully, 'Thank you, Mister Twist. Drop the Aldis and get over to the port side, stay in the lee of the chartroom. Oh, and take the quartermaster with you, we're on auto-pilot but a hit could throw the gyro so be ready to meet her. Quickly now.'

Thirty seconds . . . Please God, make those long, lean grey silhouettes out there go away and allow sanity to creep back into my nice secure little world. Or – if there's *got* to be violence and hate and madness – then let all the bloody admirals and generals do the dying . . . and bastards like J.C., and . . .

I watched the Mate going reluctantly down the ladder to the boat-deck, and I could almost feel his hurt, boyish reproach. So much so that I opened my mouth to call 'Good luck, Michael', until, during the actual moment of speaking, somehow that bloody bucko image of mine amputated the gesture to a brusque, 'Hurry, Mister! You have very little time left.'

But I didn't mean it.

Not in the way that it happened.

He was wrong too, as it turned out. Mike Ritchie, I mean. Because they didn't fire at the bridge at all – they fired at him instead.

I watched him start aft along the boat-deck and just stood there hating myself, and thinking what a bloody good student of J.C.'s I was. A real peasant-grinder supreme. The kind of ship's officer they'd have thrown into the long boat one swing ahead of Bligh R.N.

Then a tiny orange flower blossomed against the leading destroyer's fore-deck gun turret while my belly seemed to empty like a slashed water bag with the fear of it, and the incredulous disbelief that it really *was* happening after all, and that they *were* firing at us. And that Vice-Admiral Sir James Cromer was a lousy guesser as well as a grade four politician.

This time the tearing canvas sounded more like a supersonic railway train barrelling through a small bore railway tunnel, increasing during the milliseconds of its trajectory to a rushing, shrieking crescendo of energy. Then it cut . . . dead. And I had time for half a blink before a ton of Baltic Sea reared over the wing of the bridge and knocked me down, flat on my back, with the discarded Aldis cord leaping and writhing round my limbs like a terrified slow worm.

Then the explosion followed, right alongside *Venturer*'s black hull, and the whole ship trembled fifteen degrees to port so that the yellow cordite-flecked water rushed helter-skelter downhill towards the wheelhouse, piling up in greedy, exploring fingers against the break of the chartroom.

I started yelling, 'Meet her. F'r Chrissakes, *meet* her . . .!' because I could sense the bows swinging crazily over to our left, cutting right across the track of the third destroyer.

Then the ship fought back up to the vertical, and the whole bloody lot of stowaway sea on the bridge-deck came slamming back down the hill again leaping and tumbling and gurgling with excitement, until it caught me struggling to my knees and I went right under a second time while salt water curses turned to bubbles of raging frustration.

I glimpsed my new gold-braided cap hooking, for a brief moment, on the green-painted sidescreen, then it tilted to one side and fell away, sixty feet down into the subsiding blister left by the exploding shell. There was something else happening, too, but it took me a disorientated eternity of floundering around like a skate on a fisherman's deck to solve the problem.

Someone was obviously hammering, urgently and errati-cally, somewhere in the region of the boat-deck aft.

I lay there trying feebly to wipe away the seaweed strands of hair in my eyes, and staring up through the water droplets beading my eyebrows to the high, wispy tracings of mackerel cirrocumulus a remote fifty thousand feet above me. And thinking how peaceful and nice it looked up there where the only company was angels, and nobody shot at anybody, and there couldn't possibly be any bloody Russians.

Or so J.C. would have insisted.

Until the shock of the blast cleared my bruised mind and I swivelled my head to see the Second Officer scrabbling towards me through the wheelhouse on all fours, just like a great big dog . . . and the curious slamming noises aft suddenly clarified into a series of sharp explosions just as Twist's mouth opened, shouting savagely, 'They're hittin' us with light weapons, 'stead've their big stuff.'

Then his face went almost comically blank with horrified realization and he started to climb to his feet, clawing at the wheelhouse door for leverage. I still couldn't quite grasp what was happening but I did know that a man shouldn't be standing around at this end of a gunnery exercise so I started gesturing towards him, and yelling angrily, 'Get your head down, Twist. Gerrit *down*, man!'

But he just kept on rising and at the same time lunging for the after end of the bridge. 'Mike Ritchie . . .' he screamed above the crash of the shells, '. . . the Mate's still down there on the boat-deck. He'd never have made it to the ladders before . . .'

I didn't hear the rest because I found myself unwillingly scrambling to my feet too, involuntarily raising my head above the protection of the BMSNC-specified armour plate bridge screens, and the guilty sickness was in my throat as I remembered that he – Mike Ritchie – had wanted to stay up here and that *I'd* sent him aft, along the length of that exposed deck . . .

. . . until my eyes rose above the rail just as the firing

stopped, and I blinked incredulously down at the scarred, seared run of the boat-deck, with the shattered boats still hanging in their davits and the twisted ventilators gaping idiotically towards the wind, while Twist hollered stupidly, 'Christ, but the Mate's still seaworthy . . . All that an' he's still O.K.!'

I saw a fair head lift cautiously from the cover of number two boat winch, then a reefer-clad arm with three gold rings round it waved tentatively towards us as the Mate slowly stood upright and sort of felt himself all over in stunned wonderment. I started to get nervous again, the way he just stood there in the open, and threw an uneasy glance over to starboard, to where the two warships ploughed easily under control, long fore-decks dipping gracefully to the slow swell. I only had time to note that the first Russian still had his guns trained almost casually on *Venturer*'s mid-section before a movement aft caught my attention.

Someone shouted, 'Mister Ritchie . . . Hold on there,' and young, excitable Fourth Mate Timson came running up the ladder from the after well-deck.

The bad feeling I had suddenly overwhelmed me and I gripped the rail while all the muscles in the back of my neck crawled with certain anticipation. I started waving frantically and bellowing, 'Get back there, Timson! Clear the boat-deck f'r *God's* sake, laddie . . .'

Then the very thing I sensed was going to happen suddenly did, when a pretty stream of fairy lights stretched out from the flotilla leader's superstructure, feeling delicately for the particular spot where Mike Ritchie stood thanking God he was still alive.

And then he wasn't alive any more anyway, because the fairy lights turned into cannon shells, and the smart blue reefer jacket with the bright gold rings turned into an exploding crimson puff-ball of horror, spraying hideously against the white steel backdrop of the accommodation, as Chief Officer Ritchie simply blew up from his pelvis to his neck.

Timson skidded to a stunned halt, the little-boy flush bleaching to a pallid, waxy sheen as he suddenly found out that our kind of war was every bit as gruesome and violent as any stinking corpse on an official battlefield. I knew that much because, just for a brief moment, he lifted his head and gazed appealingly towards me, and I could see he was crying.

Twist blurted out agonizedly, 'Jesus help the kid!' and tried to push past me to the ladder but I grabbed his arm and, swinging him round, slammed him against the rail while grating savagely, 'Well, He's the only one who *can* help, Twist . . . Right now He's the only one who bloody can!'

But even He didn't seem to be offering us much assistance that sunny morning, because the conning fire lost interest in playing with an already dead First Mate and gradually vectored aft, chopping into, and through, the wooden planking of number four boat in a spray of flying splinters and tattered canvas. I felt my fingers digging uncontrollably into the Second Mate's thin shoulder muscles but I don't think he was even aware of my being there, not right then.

The kid was aware, though. He could see death approaching like the scudding shadow of a wind-torn cloud and, even above the cacophony of destruction, we could still hear his lost appeal. Then he spun round and his feet skidded frantically in the mess on the deck as he fought for traction – until the clouds ran on over him, and the screaming stopped, and the Fourth Mate mixed up with the First Mate in the scuppers below the colandered hull of number two starboard boat.

The firing stopped as shatteringly as it had started. And it would have been *such* a nice morning to be a sailorman otherwise, with the soft swish of the sea along our flanks and the lazily spiralling masts cutting the sky into bright blue dinner plates . . .

Twist grated monotonously, 'Bastardsbastardsbastards BASTARDS!'

59

. . . and the sparkle of the sun on polished brass fittings, and the measured, throbbing vibration of the engines carrying up through the deck, and . . .

Oh Jesus!

The *engines*!

I hurled myself through the wheelhouse door, lunging for the telegraphs. The sacrifice had been offered, the bloody slaughter performed. Ritchie and Timson and God only knew who else had made it in the Valhalla-For-Heroes-Only Stakes, so move your proudly dismembered bits and pieces over, me buckos, for it's the turn of the cowards to have their whack at staying alive . . .

The answering clang came back from below. 'Full astern both engines!' Then the revs dropped away so quickly below my feet that I knew at least one other man aboard was as keen to get home again as me. Gradually the fittings and windows around the wheelhouse started to chatter and dance as *Venturer*'s reversing screws bit deep into the oxygenated turmoil of our wake and I knew we were threshing hugely astern at last.

I hoped to God the destroyer men did too. Or Mike Ritchie and poor bloody Fourth Mate Timson with his shattered ideals and his kiddie's ebullience-turned-to-terror-spew . . . They would only be the first of many.

Somewhere outside, aft from the boat-deck, British voices were cursing in hushed, angry tones. Another voice, nearer this time, cut across the vibration and I turned to see the quartermaster, Burroughs, standing straddle-legged behind the wheel. 'I cut out the auto, Cap'n, but she won't answer any more. We've lost steerage way.'

I said gratefully, 'Thank you, Burroughs,' and looked down through the bridge windows to the flared bows, judging the moment when we were finally at rest. A movement at the starboard door and the Second Mate's flat, impassive report. 'Both dead, sir. Both officers. And the bosun has three seamen casualties aft, one serious.'

My hand shook slightly as it grasped the telegraph handle.

Forward, then back to the vertical. The repeater followed immediately. STOP BOTH ENGINES. Stop everything! Stop the bloody boat, I want to get off . . . I pivoted and stepped out on to the sun-drenched wing, trying not to see what the bosun's gang were doing with the stretchers on the boat-deck. And the buckets and hoses.

The destroyers were closing in, circling us warily now with guns still trained, but it was all right this time. I knew they weren't going to do any more killing. Not now the old lion had been stripped of his dignity and forced to bow his head in shame. Twist came out beside me and silently offered a cigarette. There wasn't anything I could do any more so I took it and lit up, and the two of us stood together in the sun and felt sad.

I blew a streamer of smoke at the Aldis lying forlornly in the corner of the wing. 'See if they've smashed that too, Mister Twist,' I muttered bitterly. 'If not, signal, I AM HOVE TO break REQUEST URGENT MEDICAL ASSISTANCE . . .'

I hesitated, wondering how you could send hate or aversion, or just plain contempt through the impersonal medium of a flashing lamp. Then I turned away and gritted in savage frustration, '. . . End of bloody message.'

A ghost moved at my elbow – one of a swelling company of dead sailormen – and I shivered. Perhaps I unwittingly foresaw that there would be more, a lot more, before he could finally rest. But how many . . .? Maybe he already knew, did that one-legged phantom. That invisibly watching Captain Viktorovich Mikhail Pritytsky, late of the Soviet Merchant Marine.

I shivered again, yet the sun was very warm.

The Russian boarding officer was angry and concerned together, in a rather uncomfortable sort of way. But tautly courteous with it.

I was just angry.

By the time he'd passed the shambles of the boat-deck and reached the top of the ladder he looked a bit white-faced. I only briefly noted the dismay and revulsion in his eyes, then ignored it because he was very young and couldn't have seen much blood before, and because those were only capitalist shreds and tatters of men back there anyway. And because I'm a cynic, and I *need* to believe that they hate us too. Just so's it makes the bloody job more bearable.

He saluted but I ignored that as well. 'First Lieutenant Fedor Yashin, Sixteenth Baltic Destroyer Flotilla, Soviet Navy . . .'

Then I found out the reason for the anger as the young Russian blurted out uncontrollably, '. . . Why did you not stop your ship, Captain? Why not, to avoid all this . . . this *waste* of men?'

I stared at him. He was blaming me, f'r Chrissake! He was actually blaming *me*. And he wasn't acting superior or overbearing or conquering, either. Just sick at all the violence. It wasn't at all what I'd expected. It made him almost like a human being. Almost. Except for the uniform.

I gestured savagely at the two Soviet ratings standing impassively behind him, with the high-planed cheek bones of the Slav – and slung sub-machine-guns. 'Keep your bloody self-justifying propaganda for the rest of the world, Mister. And get off my bridge if you haven't the guts to face up to me without a bodyguard.'

He blinked disconcertedly. Or maybe they hadn't told him that masters of British ships weren't quite as sporting as cricketers when it came to losing. I presumed he was under strict orders not to aggravate the situation any further though, because, after a barely perceptible hesitation, he half-turned and snapped a rapid order in Russian. The two sailors ramrodded to attention, then about-turned and doubled away down the ladder.

The Lieutenant faced me again and shrugged fractionally. 'I am sorry, Captain. They will go aft to assist my sick-bay attendants with your wounded.'

I said bitterly, 'I thought maybe you'd have an undertaker's rate in your Navy, Lieutenant. Like leading grave digger, first-class? To assist all the King's men . . .'

To stick First Mate Ritchie together again . . . The young kid frowned uncomprehendingly. 'The King's men, Captain? I do not quite . . .?'

I shook my head tiredly. 'It doesn't matter. It doesn't matter a damn! It was killing the poor devils in the first place which matters, Lieutenant. Like when your mates out there opened up again after you'd already ceased firing . . . We call it "Murder" in a civilized country. And stopping an unarmed merchantman in International Waters – that's called "Piracy" . . . In *any* country.'

The Russian stiffened and I could see the non-aggravation pact was almost expiring. 'I am under strict orders not to enter into any controversial discussion with you, Captain. Your complaint will no doubt be formally registered with the United Nations, and settled at diplomatic level.'

He broke off and glanced aft hesitantly, then bit his lip. 'I think you should know, however, that the second burst of fire was a mistake . . . a gunnery rating in the midships battery. He is now under close arrest while the matter is being investigated.'

I opened my mouth to say I bet *that* made Mike Ritchie and dead little Fourth Mate Timson feel a lot bloody better, but I didn't. Because I suddenly remembered that a sailor aboard a British frigate had once made a mistake, too, and that if the two incidents had run any closer a parallel, then it would have been the late Captain Brevet Cable in those buckets they were filling up on the boat-deck.

The Lieutenant recovered his poise. 'First, may I ask your name, Captain?'

I lit another Capstan without offering him one. Anyway, they all smoked samovars or something. The smoke bit into the back of my dry throat as I murmured grimly, 'Why not, Lieutenant? It's a helluva small thing to do after everything else . . . It's Cable. Captain Brevet Cable of the British Mutual Steam Navigation Company.'

I exhaled, looking at him through half-closed eyes. 'I say

again . . . *British*, Mister. D'you read me loud and clear?'

'I take your point, Captain, but you must understand you are complaining to the tail of the dog, ha? And I only wag when the head wishes me to, so please . . .'

He stopped and gazed at me, suddenly curious. 'You stress that you are British. Yet British sea captains are not noted for being stupid. And it was an extremely stupid act of bravado to refuse to heave to, especially in the knowledge that your own Royal Navy had already created a precedent by firing on our merchantman *Kuibyshev* . . .?'

I swallowed nervously. This boy was quick on the uptake. No average master *would* keep right on going with three potential destroyer broadsides suggesting he shouldn't . . .

Hurriedly I snapped, 'Didn't you say you weren't allowed to discuss anything controversial, Lieutenant? Anyway, I thought you were the wagger an' not the thinker, huh? So how's about wagging through my manifests pretty damn quick so I can continue my voyage . . . *If* you've left me with enough crewmen alive to make up a watch.'

He glanced down, suddenly rather uncomfortable for a conquering hero. 'I regret that it will not be possible. To continue your voyage, I mean.'

I knew my jaw was jutting forward fearsomely but it wasn't aggressiveness – it was the only way I could control that nervous tic of mine long enough to speak at all. And even then my voice must have sounded dangerously near to breaking point.

'*What* did you say, Mister? Just what the hell did you say about not continuing my voyage?'

At any other time I might have felt a twinge of sympathy for the Lieutenant. He wasn't at all what I wanted to think the Reds were really like, mainly because he so obviously hated shoving people around . . . or maybe *he* was only regretting *his* act of bravado in dispensing with the sub-machine-gun heavy mob before he delivered the *coup de grâce*. Either way I wasn't wasting any sympathy on anyone but me, not right then. Not even if their mother had just died.

64

Abruptly the boy's head came up and he gazed at me steadily. 'I am instructed to inform you, Captain Cable, that your ship and crew are under arrest. You will be escorted to a port in the East German Democratic Republic and handed over to the interning authorities. The vessel will be impounded and your Government informed of this action . . .'

I muttered tonelessly, 'You have no right. No bloody right at all!'

He moved to the head of the ladder and gestured resignedly. I heard the cocking lever of a *Decteriov* sub-machine-gun snick back as the two Soviet ratings warily returned to the bridge. When the Lieutenant turned to face me again a stray cat's-paw of wind ruffled his fair hair slightly and I thought, quite irrelevantly, how much like Mike Ritchie he looked as he stood there silently, not even wasting an answer. I think he'd finally realized there wasn't much point in talking any more.

Not that he really had to, anyway. Because you don't need to be nice, or even in the right. Not when you have all the guns on your side.

In actual fact there was an awful lot of talking done over the next nine days – usually in a squalid little cell in the basement of what appeared to be some form of East German Military establishment.

I never did find out where I was for sure. I just watched critically, and noted quite a lot of navigational data in a surreptitious sort of way, as their pilot conned *Venturer* up to a berth in the Baltic port of Ahldenstadt. Then, as soon as we'd made fast, I was gun-prodded all the way down to a black van waiting on the wharf and driven away to God knows where. It took three hours of not looking out of the truck windows because there weren't any, and settling instead for three weary hours of staring down the automatic rifle barrel pointed unwaveringly at me by an apparently deaf mute of an East German Army *Feldwebel*.

And, like I said, another nine days of listening to people who didn't believe me when I insisted I was just an ordinary captain of an ordinary ship caught up in a most extra-bloody-ordinary breach of International fuckin' *law*, f'r Chris . . .

First, there was a guard with an incurable thirst for knowledge which seemed to far exceed a normal warder's interests – but he kept on calling me 'Herr Goebbel', which didn't do all that much to cement good Anglo-Deutsch relations for a start.

Then there was a fat little cretin in a black policeman's uniform who looked more like a refugee from the executive suite of Dachau. And he kept screaming 'Capitalist filth!' for absolutely no reason at all.

Or there was the terribly suave, cold Russian MVD colonel who called me simply 'Captain Cable'. But also asked questions with an icy precision which left me bathed in terrified sweat at the end of every session.

And, finally, that creepy, seedy little man in the old, stained raincoat, who spoke like an Oxford Don and breathed halitosis fumes all over me while smiling to reveal sharp, almost canine teeth. *He* called me 'Brevet, old chap', yet I somehow knew that he was the most dangerous of the lot . . .

. . . But then – on the tenth day – a Chinese People's Army lieutenant a few thousand miles away gave an order to fire a 70 millimeter howitzer from the Chinese side of the Ussuri River. The shell landed, as had many others, on the Sino-Russian disputed territory called Damansky Island. In fact, the only real difference was that it also landed smack on the steel helmet of a visiting Soviet field-marshal called something-or-other Bosnik.

It was the yellow straw which finally broke the Russian Bear's back. To say nothing of the tattered bloody mess it had made of the late Field-Marshal Bosnik.

By midnight of that day seven divisions of Soviet mechanized infantry had crossed the Mongolian border and were engaged in fierce fighting with the Chinese hordes who, in their turn, threw a hell of a lot of stuff back, all labelled 'High explosive. Made in Pekin.'

It still wasn't a *proper* war, but it was a bloody good imitation.

My unexpected reprieve came when it also made the Soviets think more deeply about pushing their luck on two fronts so – to mollify those hawks in the British Government who were unsportingly advocating stabbing the Reds in the back while we could still push the buttons – the Kremlin ordered the release and repatriation of *British Venturer*'s crewmen.

They kept the ship, but we had to let them save a little face so we didn't argue.

I had one candid and deeply satisfying crack at the little bastard in the black suit, then flew back to London the next day along with a relieved Second Mate Twist and a crowd of coarsely gesturing and utterly unrepentant British seamen.

I've never been so glad to see home again as I was then, and thought it was pretty decent of the yellow devils to go to all that trouble just to get Cable out of his latest mess – or maybe they'd had a few other reasons, as well. But I didn't mind a bit. That was the nice thing about being a coward – you feel so damn relieved when you're safe again.

Or at least, I assumed I was.

Because I'd overlooked a lonely ship, still lying in an unfriendly country. A suddenly dangerous, deadly ship.

A ship called *British Venturer*.

Four

'. . . while the Sino-Soviet situation's still worsening from day to day.' J.C. leant forward and smiled frostily, 'You're a damn sight luckier than you seem to realize, Cable. Not every apprehended British seaman gets released by the Kremlin because five hundred million Chinamen are pounding hard enough on Ivan's back door to encourage a magnanimous gesture towards the West.'

I said woodenly, 'Oh, yessir. Very lucky.' And thought about Mike Ritchie and the Timson kid.

The Admiral leaned back, watching me speculatively. He seemed to have something on his mind but I wasn't really interested in *his* current problems. All I wanted to do was wind up the de-briefing, dodge the crowd of pressmen and photographers lined up outside the BMSNC office entrance, and absorb the first good night's sleep I'd had for the past three weeks or so – ever since I'd so generously been given what must have proved the shortest command in the Merchant bloody Navy.

And the most hectic.

Standing behind J.C., McReadie seemed to read my thoughts. 'Sorry about the ship, Brev?'

I shrugged fractionally. 'It's not a bundle of fun, being given a ship, then getting pistol-prodded right off her bridge into the local jug before you've even time to lay out your clean collars – no.'

The Admiral inspected a pencil with intense interest. 'You were left alone to watch while their pilot took *Venturer* into Ahldenstadt, weren't you, Captain?'

'More or less . . . if you discount the assorted Slavonic bluejackets with the weaponry who hung around the after end of the bridge just daring me to run her aground.'

Then everything started to go wrong as usual when, without the slightest trace of a smile, McReadie said, 'So why didn't you try?'

I blinked disconcertedly. 'Why didn't I try what?'

'To run her aground, Captain.' The Admiral's voice sliced across the room.

I pivoted and stared at him incredulously as he repeated sharply, 'Run *British Venturer* aground, Cable. Preferably on the edge of deep water where she would have broken up and sunk . . .'

'. . . and saved us all a hell of a lot of trouble. One helluva lot of trouble,' McReadie finished emphatically.

I closed my eyes momentarily and tried to catch up. Here I was, the conquered hero home from the enemy sea – a real life International Incident who'd successfully defied shot and shell in the finest traditions of the British Merchant Service – yet the very people who should be proud of me were now asking, quite seriously, why I hadn't done a *Graf Spee* on the Reds and scuttled my ship to keep her out of Soviet hands.

Just to save *trouble*. Meaning, presumably, a few weeks of diplomatic negotiation to secure the inevitable return of what was – if you discounted my personal interest in her – only a clapped-out old bucket anyway, and one which BMSNC could easily replace with yet another surreptitious dip into the taxpayer's pocket.

If that was what they meant.

Then I noticed the faces of the two men opposite, and I realized it wasn't, and my nerve ends started to shrivel in frightened anticipation. Because I suddenly knew that Cable hadn't quite finished with his first command after all. And that I'd been right that time so long ago on *Venturer*'s bridge, while the bits and pieces of two young officers still slowly dried under the Baltic sun, and the Red destroyers circled warily. And I'd shivered uncontrollably as a ghost looked over my shoulder, whispering, 'How many more, Cable? How many more deaths before this is over . . .?'

Until the little Admiral placed his hands on the table, stared grimly at me, and said quite matter-of-factly, 'You have forty-eight hours, Mister. Forty-eight hours to learn a lot of new skills. Before you go back to the Baltic with another mission in mind . . . to steal *British Venturer* right from under the Soviet nose!'

I started to swear. Softly at first, then, as the frustrated hurt of all they'd already put me through welled to the surface, more and more violently until the obscenities were tumbling from my mouth in a cataract of viciousness.

Until I finally ground to an exhausted halt while – across the table – a double-crossing ex-admiral blinked placidly and said, with a trace of boredom, 'Finished, Cable? Or are you only having a rest before you start again?'

I slumped back in my chair and shook my head. It just occurred to me that I'd been taking a bigger chance then than when I'd stared down those destroyer gun barrels and, anyway, he'd taken it all so disinterestedly that I hadn't even enjoyed the glow of satisfaction you get from delivering a succintly insulting broadside.

Which proved J.C. was a good psychologist as well as a fu . . .

'Why . . .?' I muttered to no one in particular, 'Why did you want to make a present of *Venturer* to the Soviets only a few days ago yet now, all of a sudden, she's become a hot property? Now all the shouting's dying down anyway?'

The Admiral nodded abruptly to McReadie who moved forward, for the first time. I noticed, as he started to speak, that he looked pretty haggard too. Like a man with a worry. It didn't take long to find out just how big a worry that was.

'Cast your mind back to the political situation as it was a few weeks ago, Cable. Before the Chinese started to put the squeeze on the Ussuri River border area.'

'You mean when the only tension was between us and them – the Russians?'

J.C. wriggled in his chair. 'Tension is an understatement.

We were damn nearly at war . . . Do you realize that, within two hours of *Venturer*'s arrest, the Cabinet had prepared the full mobilization proclamation to be placed before Parliament?'

I shook my head cynically. 'I had a few other things on my mind. Like being arrested along with the bloody ship.'

The Admiral stabbed a finger at me. 'Sir,' he said flatly.

'Sir.' I ground out reluctantly. It signalled that I'd used up all the tolerance I was going to get.

McReadie continued, 'When you took *Venturer* east of thirteen east – into the Soviet restricted area – there were two possible results . . .' He ticked them off on his fingers. '. . . One. They accepted that we'd called their bluff and backed down – like when their Cuban missile carrier aborted under the Kennedy threat. Or . . . Two. That they carried out their intentions and impounded your ship in either an East German or Polish port – which they actually did.'

I muttered impulsively, 'There's a third alternative, McReadie. Not that it would apparently have bothered you . . . that those destroyers lobbed in a few more rounds and sent me and my crew to the bottom of the Baltic.'

'We couldn't have *been* that lucky!'

McReadie's features had flushed an angry, resentful red while the hairline scar formed a savagely purple contrast. I stared at him in shocked surprise – all right, so maybe I had been a bit sharp, but didn't I have the right? And personalities had never entered into our relationship before.

'I said we couldn't have been that lucky.' He looked right into my eyes and he didn't seem like a friend anymore. 'I wish to God they had, Cable . . . Yeah, even if it'd meant leaving you with your guts stringing out below your lifejacket!'

The nervous tic started tugging at the side of my face as I felt the temper welling up inside me, overkilling even the misery. I gazed at McReadie coldly for what seemed a very long time, then quite deliberately turned my back on him, facing J.C. The Admiral's brow furrowed warningly but I didn't give a damn any more, not even if he intended showing me out of the sixteenth-floor window to the street.

'Why . . .?' I grated tightly, '. . . Just why *do* you want *Venturer* hijacked? Just what was she carrying that you . . . ah . . . forgot to tell me about? *Sir.*'

He didn't even allow his eyes to flicker, not once. He wasn't going to be hurried, either. 'First you must appreciate that – had the Chinese not attacked so unexpectedly – we might well have been negotiating with the Soviet Union on the brink of war by now . . . And your ship would still have been held in any one of a number of highly populated and strategically valuable ports . . .'

A droplet of sweat ran down the side of my nose and splashed on his highly polished desk top. The wet little star was obliterated as my hand smashed down on it. 'What . . . was . . . she . . . carrying . . . dammit?'

The pencil snapped between his fingers.

'All right. But it's not *was*, because she still does at this minute, Cable. Welded into her number four hold forward deep tank . . . a thermo-nuclear device bigger than anything we can possibly deliver by ICBM or air strike . . .

'. . . It means that *British Venturer* is virtually a gigantic floating bomb.'

I swamped my face with another gout of icy water then just leant against the wall, staring at myself in the washroom mirror and thinking what a naïve, idiot I'd really turned out to be.

Or maybe I was just sluicing away the tensions of two weeks of fear. Just so's I could make room for the next bloody intake.

McReadie's reflection moved awkwardly behind me, almost embarrassed. 'I suppose I should say I'm sorry, Brev. About that . . . in there?'

I rinsed my mouth out and spat into the basin and felt a bit better. 'I suppose you should too, McReadie. But forget it. You and him, you've done too many things to apologize for . . . and this isn't a first time for BMSNC anyway, is it?'

He frowned. 'What isn't?'

I dabbed my face with the taut band of material they laughingly call a roller towel. The kind that, as soon as you try to pull off a clean bit, everything inside the bloody machine seizes up and leaves you with hardly any. '. . . Sending a ship into a Red port with an atomic bomb as supercargo! To give our diplomatic boys an ace card to negotiate with if the other side gets too stroppy.'

I saw, in the mirror, the way his mouth turned up slightly at the corners and knew the old McReadie grin would be there in a minute. 'Hydrogen,' he said.

'What?'

'The bombs – they're not atomic – they're hydrogen. Helium produced by fusion of the atomic nuclei of the heavy water isotopes deuterium and . . . ah . . . tritium. Atom bombs are kiddie's stuff in comparison – just a straight-forward subjecting to fission of either the uranium isotope $U235$ or – like in the Nagasaki drop – the artificial element plutonium $Pu239$ . . .'

I snapped, 'F'r Christ's sake, McReadie! You make it sound like making up a cough prescription at the local chemist.'

He really did grin then, but there wasn't an awful lot of humour in it. 'It still stops you coughing, though.'

'And you still haven't answered my question – we *have* done this before, haven't we?'

'Twice . . .' He chewed his lip thoughtfully, watching me carefully. 'The first time was a long way back – in Odessa during the Cuban crisis. Then the second was when *British Regiment* loaded animal hides in Nanking while Mao tried to pressurize Hong Kong. Remember? Only they weren't needed – not even diplomatically – so they sailed back home with no one any the wiser.'

I nodded at the mirror, then turned and looked at him. 'Including their captains? I mean, did *their* masters know what they had down below . . . or did you an' J.C. con them into thinking *they* were just making an ordinary voyage too?'

McReadie stopped grinning and gazed straight back. 'What d'you think, Brev? F'rinstance, could you really still act as a conventional ship's master, knowing you were riding a fifty megaton tiger . . .?'

I felt the mock buoyancy draining out of me and I wanted to be sick again. '*Fifty* megat . . .! My God man, but that's . . . F'r cryin' out loud, McReadie, a thing like that would evaporate the whole bloody Baltic!'

He shrugged imperceptibly. 'So now you know why I was a bit edgy in there.'

I muttered numbly, 'You're mad! The whole screwed-up lot of you. Mad as hatters . . . Aw, just count me out, McReadie. I've resigned. Kaput! Get stuffed, you an' him both!'

The Commander moved up behind me and watched me warily in the mirror. 'You're already in over your head. Look, who d'you think is the most guilty in a murder pact, Cable – the gunsmith who supplies the gun or the heavy who actually pulls the trigger?'

I swung round and pushed him away violently. 'You mean that because I drove the ship, then I pulled the trigger, don't you? But you're not on, mate! 'Cause I didn't have a clue.'

He raised an eyebrow mockingly. 'Oh? And who'd believe it, Captain? After you'd personally delivered *Venturer* into a place called Ahldenstadt. A place with a million people living almost on top of it.'

A familiar, one-legged ghost stroked my spine with sub-zero fingers. 'I was arrested, dammit. I was forced to go there.'

'After you'd refused several orders to heave to – yes. One construction could be that you had even provoked the Soviets into escorting you in . . . left them with no alternative.'

We glowered at each other for a moment then, miserably, I dropped my eyes. There wasn't a lot of point in dragging

74

it out any longer. I knew already that I was going back to the Baltic, but I just had to have one more answer. 'But why the skull and crossbones bit? The super hijack? Why not just leave her there and negotiate for her return through diplomatic channels?'

He shrugged. 'That's what we've been doing – until now. But the situation's changed suddenly. Someone in Whitehall is leaking classified information across the curtain . . . this year's routine spy scare. Special Branch'll have the bastard pretty soon but we can't take the chance that the Soviets haven't been tipped-off that *Venturer* just may be a little more than an ordinary freighter. Any close examination will soon show she's explosive material in more ways than one.'

I followed him down the corridor, back towards J.C.'s operations room. It was like I said – I'd known all the time that I would be going back to the ship I'd once commanded, but McReadie would have been so disappointed if he hadn't had to threaten, and even blackmail a little, first.

And anyway, there *was* my reluctant hero's image to think of.

We started planning. J.C. called it OPERATION STAYSAIL because he was Service-orientated and they had to have an obscure label for everything.

I wasn't, so I just called it a typical shambles. Under my breath.

There was one burning question I had to know the answer to first, apart from why in God's name they'd had to pick on me. And that was – what was the real point of the mission anyway? When, and if, we ever got aboard *Venturer*, what were we supposed to do then – ditch the bomb, tow the ship away, or bring her home all dismantled and packed in a suitcase?

Naturally the answer was in Admiralty Chart Number 2816, Baltic Sea. I'd seen it so often before that I was getting to the stage where I didn't need it.

J.C. leaned over and gestured. 'You'll sail *Venturer* out of

75

Ahldenstadt, Cable . . .'

He saw me opening my mouth to protest and held up his hand warningly. 'Later. But rest assured, you'll be sailing her out under her own power . . . Now. Thirty-two miles will bring you to the eastern tail of the Oder Bank . . .' He stabbed the chart just above the Niechorze Light. I noted automatically that it had a twenty mile visibility but it wouldn't really matter to me – we were going to be less than ten miles off the Polish coast there, anyway. And any guns they happened to have handy.

The Admiral changed into top gear. 'From there you alter to the nor'-east. A run of sixteen miles and you'll have made good the twenty fathom line. Another few minutes on that heading and you're in thirty fathoms plus – over two hundred feet of water under your keel . . .'

McReadie said quietly, 'It means a total of two hours and ten minutes steaming from the Ahldenstadt fairway buoy. At emergency full ahead.'

There were too many questions. Far too many. I muttered nervously, 'Then what? When she's in all that water?'

'We can't run the risk of another interception by the Soviet Navy. And every minute you're afloat in the Baltic increases their chances of finding you – That's why you'll be carrying two demolition experts. They'll have had ample time to prepare . . .' J.C. made a little chopping motion with his hand, '. . . at zero seven hundred hours, two days from today, you'll blow the bottom right out of your ship.'

The more I thought about this crazy operation the more it seemed to me like my other favourite nightmare – flying. I mean, the bit in the middle isn't too bad, it's just the taking off and landing that scares the hell out of me. And it was the same with OPERATION STAYSAIL . . . I could face with reasonable equanimity the idea of steaming like a bat out of Hades for fifty miles in the middle of the night – even dodging Polish shells, East German patrol boats and most of the Russian Navy while I was doing it – but the beginning

76

and end of *Venturer*'s last mad voyage – with all the violence and nastiness, and sheer physical terror that *those* particular phases were bound to incorporate . . .

And all the time riding the potential ten million degrees of heat generated by a probably completely unstable hydrogen device. Big enough to lift me, *Venturer* and half-a-dozen square miles of sea up on to the top of a ten thousand foot mushroom . . .?

I said bitterly, 'Then what? When I've scuttled myself? It's a helluva big tank of water, the Baltic.'

McReadie scratched his head annoyingly. 'Submarine. There'll be an *Oberon* Class boat waiting to rendezvous with you as you abandon ship. They're lousy waters to operate in – not enough depth to fill your boots in places – but they'll manage.'

Only it wasn't submarine difficulties I was worrying about so much as *British Venturer*, and there were still a lot of other problems. Like how did we get the ship out of Ahldenstadt in the first place? According to J.C., we had to recover it the hard way – and steal it so that they didn't even know who the lightfingered sailormen were.

Which was impossible. Wasn't it?

McReadie shrugged. 'We don't think so. Not under the circumstances in which you'll operate.'

'Which are?'

The Admiral stood up, and, moving round the desk, leaned against it with folded arms. 'You ever heard of a group called *Wiedereinstellung*, Cable? Roughly translated from the German it means reinstatement . . . "To restore again to a former state or position".'

'You said it was a group, not an intention.'

He smiled fractionally. 'It's both, Cable. It's a group with an intention – to unify Germany and restore it to its previous national station in the world. It's an illegal organization, however – in both East and West Germany.'

I frowned. 'You mean they're some form of underground? Resistance fighters and that?'

'More or less. Though they haven't done much fighting to date. They're too careful and methodical. They're planners as yet, Cable, in the good old Teutonic tradition.'

'But if this . . . this organization are that keen to give the Reds the heave then why are the West Germans so set against them? Surely that's what the Bonn crowd want – reunification with the East?'

J.C. shook his head. 'Not the way the *Wiedereinstellung* propose. You see, they want to engineer not only the fall of Communist influence in the East but also the complete overthrow of the present Federal Republican Government and a return to power of the *Nationalsozialistische Deutsche Arbeiter Partei . . .*'

McReadie must have seen me looking irritably lost because he said quickly, 'In other words, they're *Nazis*. Hitlerites. Planning and preparing all over again like subterranean slugs, all ready to stick their death's heads out from under the stones an' proclaim the glorious Fourth Reich. They're about to rise again, Cable.'

I grinned uncertainly. 'You're kidding, McReadie. All right, there may still be a few around, I grant you – but not in enough numbers to present more than a temporary annoyance to the authorities. And they wouldn't be crazy enough to show themselves anyway – hell, the Soviets would clean them out in no time once they came out into the open . . .'

J.C. caught up again silkily, like a cat with illicit cream on its face. 'But not if they were only rising in preparation for an immediate NATO assault on East Germany, Cable. Not if the new Nazis thought that we were right behind them in a determined effort to dislodge the Russians by launching a pre-emptive strike from the Baltic while they were fully occupied in fighting the Chinese on their Far Eastern Front.'

I stared at him in petulant disbelief. 'But you just told me that the Government had decided *not* to intervene in the Sino-Soviet business. And that it's only to avoid more trouble with the Kremlin that we're supposed to be pulling

Venturer out from under their noses in the first place . . .'

The Admiral smiled. A slow, wolfish, terribly dishonest smile. '*You* know that, Captain, and *I* know that. But there are thirty thousand new-look Nazis – over five thousand of them in the Ahldenstadt area alone – and they don't know that, Cable. Because they don't know anything other than what we choose to tell them . . .'

It was fantastic, admittedly – but it was also so much of a perfect J.C. double-cross that even I gradually became convinced that it might work. And that made a first time for me, too, being normally cast as the spanner in the works during these BMSNC strategy planning sessions.

I still tried hard to find the flaws. I mean, if there was an unseen snag then I was going to be the first to find out. Probably when the bullet hit me. But it was like firing a battery of questions against a wall of imperturbable answers, and all of them good. If you didn't have a weak stomach. I probed. 'Just to go over the ground again . . . You really intend to convince thirty thousand East Germans that, by rising against the Soviet Occupation Forces, they are making the first move in an immediately impending NATO offensive. Correct?'

He shook his head, looking rather pleased with himself. 'They already have been convinced, Cable. We have . . . ah . . . recently negotiated certain terms with them regarding the future government of a free Germany.'

McReadie sniffed. 'Except that, under the new Nazis, maybe freedom isn't quite as you and I see it, Cable. They've already got their embryo Gestapo sections planning another *putsch* on the "dissident factions" . . . by courtesy of the British and US Governments, of course. Or so they think.'

I said sarcastically, 'Nice people. Just the sort we want as Allies, naturally.'

The Admiral's eyes narrowed dangerously and he leaned over towards me. 'Any day now the Soviets may decide to take a closer look at *British Venturer* . . . which means we can't risk leaving her in their hands a moment longer than necessary. And by God but I'd tip my cap to the Devil himself if I thought he could help get her out of there. Do you understand me, Cable? Loud and clear?'

I bit my lip. 'Then may I ask how this . . . this alliance is going to help?'

'By creating a diversion.' McReadie was talking now. 'Primarily by pulling what defensive units the Reds have in Ahldenstadt away from the dock area to allow your Operation Staysail team the time you need to get aboard and run *Venturer* out into the Baltic.'

It made sense. So far. I frowned doubtfully. 'And what do our Nazi oppo's use to fight with? Or do they throw rocks?'

McReadie grinned down at me. 'I said earlier that they'd been planning a long time, Cable, which they have. And we've been helping them just a little – in the Red-occupied Democratic Republic only, of course. But our Swastika-waving friends are now sitting on an arsenal of weapons that would make any emergent nation jealous as hell . . . anti-tank rockets, battalion level machine-guns, mines, grenades, automatic rifles, small arms . . .'

I said sharply, 'The Russians have got tanks, McReadie. Bloody great tanks! And personnel carriers. And artillery an' close air support. *And*, without even reinforcing them, maybe ten infantrymen to every one the Germans can muster . . .'

J.C. snapped, 'They're *Nazis*, Cable. A million times worse than the Soviets.'

I swung round on him angrily. 'They're still people, Admiral. So after we've taken *Venturer* out, then what? What happens to the thirty thousand believers who're left firing nine millimetre pistols against four inch armour-plated flame throwers?'

His face cleared until, when he finally spoke, his voice was surprisingly mild. 'They'll probably be liquidated, Cable. All thirty thousand of them. But it's still infinitely cheaper than a premium of maybe half a million cremated corpses if you fail to recover *Venturer*. Because if you do . . .

'. . . we are left with no alternative but to strike first, and to detonate that bomb!'

I sat there for what seemed a very long time, trying to digest it all. It seemed so incredible, so utterly fantastic to think that, when I was a young kid still full of the wonderment and fascination of the sea, the majority of my waking hours – and a large part of my restlessly sleeping ones – had been spent in watching and waiting for the spine-telescoping crash of a torpedo ripping through our double-bottoms. A Nazi torpedo, fired on the order of men who were hated and feared by anyone who believed in democracy and human decency, and in the right to live.

Yet now, less than half that lifetime later, I was preparing to call them allies? Because there was a greater enemy, and we needed all the help we could get, and the weapons. Even the dirty ones. Oh, I'd heard the phrase before. It was called 'Expedient'. But I already knew all about that.

McReadie passed me a cigarette and blew a long streamer of smoke at the ceiling. 'You'll be fully briefed on the *Wiedereinstellung* alliance later. But think about it, Brev. You'll see it makes sense.'

I didn't answer. I already knew it made sense. It not only meant that we had thirty thousand self-elected clay pigeons to cover for us but that, as an extra no sweat bonus, J.C. had engineered the suicide of an embryo terror that otherwise could arise like some obscene Phoenix from the ashes of Belsen and Dachau and Buchenwald – only maybe, next time, the ovens would be nuclear powered.

Oh, it made sense, all right. But so does any war. From the planner's point of view.

I said tentatively, 'You mentioned the Staysail *team* earlier, Commander – which presumably means that you aren't just relying on me and thirty thousand mini-Fuhrers to hijack *Venturer*.'

He grinned placidly. 'There are maybe a quarter of a

million trained soldiers in the Soviet Zone, Cable boy. How many of ours would you suggest you need as a bodyguard?'

I shrugged diffidently. 'How about half a million, then? Plus air support, carriers, guided missile destroy . . .'

J.C. snapped irritably, 'You have twelve. Excluding yourself, of course.'

But then, he never did have a sense of humour. And neither did I – not any more.

McReadie filled in. 'Firstly, you need enough specialists to take *Venturer* to sea. We're giving you a Chief Engineer and a Mate . . . You already know one of them.'

'Being?'

'Twist. Your late Second Mate. He's dead keen to go along with you and he already knows the ship . . . and he seems to think he has a score to settle over what happened to your First and Fourth Officers last time.'

'Then he's a bigger bloody fool than I thought he was.' But I still felt pleased to have young Twist along, all the same. He'd shaped up pretty well that last time, up there on *Venturer*'s bridge, and I was going to need someone with a good, dedicated hate worked up to help me run that gauntlet to the thirty fathom line.

'And the Chief? Who's he?'

'A damn good engineer as well as a solid stayer. Name's Reid – just promoted from Second on the old *Allegiance*. D'you know him?'

I shook my head. All I hoped was that I was going to live long enough to get to know the whole lot of them. 'That's three of us. Who else? Like, who's going to light the fuses after we've done the driving? *And* make damn sure that . . . that monstrosity of yours doesn't trigger itself off at the same time?'

I noted a glance pass between them but J.C. answered quickly, 'We're giving you two Royal Marine AEs. They're the best in the demolition business.'

'AEs?'

'Assault Engineers. They'll punch the bottom out of her

like an electric tin opener.'

McReadie said cheerfully, 'And to show there's no expense spared you're getting another six Marine Commandos as well – an officer, Colour sergeant and four squaddies. They're all seconded volunteers, and all specialists . . .'

I cut in bleakly, 'In what, Commander? What do they specialize in?'

He gazed back dispassionately. The fleeting humour was gone. 'In killing people, Cable. Very quietly indeed.'

I started sweating, even though I felt cold and shivery inside. This wasn't my line at all. Not this killing so close you could actually *see* a man's eyes staring beseechingly, or feel the drag of scrabbling, pleading hands as they slipped nervelessly away from your wrists . . . I muttered, 'That makes eleven, including me. So what are the other two – undertakers?'

They glanced at each other again. This time I could even feel the hairs prickling on the back of my neck. Obviously it was surprise time for Cable again and I knew I wasn't going to like it. I glowered at the Admiral and repeated the question. Savagely.

'The other two . . . *Sir?*'

For the first time I noticed the lines of strain in his face, pulling tiredly at the resolute, slightly bad tempered mouth. He looked frail and worn right then. But only for a moment.

'One of them is an Army Ordnance Corps Major. From the Central Weapons Command Laboratory.'

The nervous tic came back and I knuckled the corner of my eye angrily. 'Why him? I thought we had our blow-up boys all lined up already?'

His answer, when it came, surprised even me by the venom of its delivery. 'They still can't disarm a booby-trapped thermo-nuclear bomb, Cable. And, God help you . . . that's just what you're going to have to do. Before you sink your ship.'

McReadie was the thirteenth man, of course. I mean, I

83

should have guessed that this latest foray was right up the street of a buccaneering Anglo-Saxon like him. And I bet my tropical whites to a Chinaman's underpants that the chance to make Cable's Commando up to a nice, unlucky thirteen was enough incentive in itself.

And who needed bad luck when they already had a hydrogen bomb which was now, apparently, also the most anti of anti-personnel devices in the long and bloody history of warfare?

In fact, who needed bad luck when they already had McReadie?

I remember staring dully at J.C.'s set face, and muttering with difficulty, 'Booby trap? You mean, the bomb's liable to . . .?'

Then McReadie had jumped in quickly to say he was going too, but I'd shouted I didn't give a bloody toss if *he* went to hell on a bicycle, but what was all this about a somethin' or other BOOBY TRAP . . .?

Until J.C. had slammed the desk like a man who hated desks, and roared, 'Belay that, Cable! There's only one thing which terrifies me more than the thought of having that bomb go off on Communist territory, dammit . . . and that's having it discovered, reinstalled in a Russian ship and counter-infiltrated to devastate the entire south-east coast of England any time *they* want to watch *us* burn!'

I snarled back uncaringly, 'So now you're trying to tell me the Soviets haven't got a few nuclear weapons of their own without salvaging ours second-hand?'

'Damn right they have! But they still don't have a device like that one in *British Venturer*, thank God . . . They don't have a bomb which can be sailed into any port in the world yet still remain undetected by the most sophisticated spy apparatus in existence today. A bomb which could crisp the whole of the Metropolitan area of London into a charcoal smear without even raising a shudder in a Geiger counter needle at zero minus one.'

McReadie broke in. Determinedly this time. 'It means

that, given planned strategic deployment, every existing ICBM and MIRV and all the other methods of delivering high-speed death are already obsolete, Cable. Along with the early warning systems and DEWLINE and the detector satellites . . . because you can't detect the undetectable. Not when it could be imported in every ship, every trans-Continental lorry . . .'

'Not unless you pull them all apart.' The Admiral muttered, 'Right down to a pile of nuts, bolts and rivets. And paralyse a whole transport system while you do so.'

McReadie spread his hands. 'The alternative is living with the fear of death every time you see anything bigger than a baby's pram rolling in through the ports.'

'Or we can destroy *Venturer*, Cable. One way or the other . . .' J.C. leaned back heavily and shrugged, '. . . before they find out too, about how to kill a country so it doesn't even know the war's started.'

I moved to the door and opened it. I was learning too many things too suddenly. Turning back I gazed at the two men for a moment. 'I'm going to see a man about a booby trap,' I said bitterly. 'An' a few other things which are making me sick to my guts right this minute.'

McReadie called, 'I'm coming with you.'

I walked out without waiting. 'That, McReadie, is one of the things I bloody mean.'

But, really, I was glad. I had the feeling that I would need his company when it came round to dying time.

Five

'The basic requirement for nuclear fusion, Captain, is an enormously high temperature – several million degrees, in point of fact.'

I looked bleakly at my twelfth man as he sat, comfortably relaxed, in what was somewhat ambitiously referred to as the 'Senior Officers (Seagoing) Recreation Room', and was now – temporarily – nominated as the STAYSAIL Briefing Centre.

'Centigrade or Fahrenheit, Major?'

He smiled a little wintrily. 'With respect, Captain, as you and I will be immediately adjacent to the heat source in the event of its premature activation, I would suggest that your question is somewhat . . . ah . . . academic.'

Then, unexpectedly, the rather studious, aquiline features dissolved into a grin and he added, 'Let's just say it'll absolutely ruin the trip. For everyone.'

I blinked disconcertedly at the idea of a scientist with a sense of humour, then decided that anyone who worked with hydrogen bombs as a career just had to be able to see the silver lining to every mushroom cloud, and began to grin doubtfully too. I bet thinking out bigger and better ways of blowing more and more people up must have been a giant bundle of fun, down at Central Weapons Command Laboratories.

Like Monopoly, only with people for properties and megatons for money.

The Major chuckled all the way to the coffee percolator. I watched him pour and said decisively, 'Black. Three sugars.' Then, more tentatively, 'This . . . ah . . . *Venturer* bomb. How does it work?'

He turned, carrying a cup with the same care he would have afforded a flask of nitro-glycerine. 'How does it work? You must be kidding, Captain . . . or have a passionate interest in nuclear physics.'

I went back to being irritated. 'I mean – how were we supposed to trigger it if the balloon had really gone up? Or, of more immediately selfish interest – how do we *not* trigger it when we make the snatch?'

Gray cocked his head to one side and looked very professional. 'We incorporated three entirely independent initiating devices into this particular mark of device . . . The primary first strike system – the one used in the event of a deliberate, remote-controlled war demand – is by coded ultra-sonic radio transmission. The coded firing sequence was, of course, computer-calculated and is virtually impossible to reproduce by accident, even if the frequencies themselves are duplicated . . .'

I said sharply, '*Virtually* impossible?'

His mouth turned up at the corners a little. 'As a Fail-Safe measure the trigger mechanism requires *two* independent and simultaneous U/S transmissions . . . and from two entirely divorced Ministry of Defence top security underground bunkers.'

'Say the Soviets hit us first? Take out one or both of our activating transmitters?'

It was like arguing with J.C. All the answers had been worked out before I even started. 'The trigger systems have been duplicated, Captain. As a second strike retaliatory measure there are two Polaris submarines somewhere out there with an identical capacity for remotely initiating the device . . . and standing orders to do so if they ever launch their own ICBM flock.'

I muttered sickly, 'An undetectable trigger for an undetectable bomb. It's good, Major. Sneaky, but very, very good . . . if you can live with it.'

He shrugged diffidently. 'There are over fifty million people in this country who may infinitely prefer that to the alternative of dying without it, Captain.'

I glanced at my watch. There were other things more pressing than a Brevet Cable treatise on morality – even if I could have thought up the arguments I just knew, somehow, were there somewhere. 'Didn't you say there were three firing systems?'

Gray nodded. 'The second is merely a variation of the primary ultra-sonic radio initiator – with a time delay . . . Like the World War Two delayed action mines.'

'You mean the codes are sent but the bang doesn't come till later?'

'Exactly. With a slight modification of the original transmission sequence . . . Really it's largely a political expedient. To allow time for evacuation of the area while our negotiators are busy trying to convince the Soviets that they unknowingly nurse a lot more vipers in Mother Russia's bosom . . . The Cabinet hope that one salutory demonstration of our already-delivered striking power can persuade them to hold off their own pre-emptive moves . . . Call it a day because they've lost the initiative before they even start shooting.'

I shrugged. 'But we don't *have* any more *Venturer*'s, do we?'

He shrugged again. 'No. But they'd have to be pretty certain of that, because you can't intercept a threat that's already arrived . . . and how can they be?'

'And the delayed action? How long?'

'Forty-eight hours precisely. Its count-down is accurate to the ten-thousandth part of a second . . . and unalterable.'

My coffee suddenly tasted bitter as hell. 'You can't evacuate half a country in forty-eight hours, Major. Not even in forty-eight days hardly.'

He drained his cup approvingly. But then, he was more used to the idea of cremating people by the living city-full than me. 'No. But you *can* sail, or tow, the bomb carrier away from the population centres, once you know where it is. And the end product – the demonstration value – remains every bit as impressive.'

I shook my head. 'Not from the Baltic, you couldn't. Not with the traffic around there, unless you broke every navigational rule in the book. Not in two days.'

Gray stopped smiling and sat just a little stiffer in his chair. 'I wouldn't know. I'm just the builder's labourer, I don't decide on the firm's policy.'

It's funny how modest people can get when the question of responsibility becomes involved. I chewed my lip. 'And the third trigger . . . ? Presumably the . . . ah . . . booby trap?'

He looked disapproving. 'We prefer to call it the Anti-Tampering and Destruct Mechanism, actually . . .' Then his features crinkled into another of those unexpected grins as he said, '. . . and by God but it stops you clowning about with other people's Meccano sets for a hobby!'

I frowned gloomily and just hoped it was only a perverted sense of humour and not an unbalanced brain that caused these splurges of black hilarity. He continued a little apologetically, 'To put it in a nutshell, old boy, it means that – if the infernal machine's opened up to expose its innards – then whoever's curious won't ever be able to report back to his senior boffins. Mind you, it's an obvious precaution in view of the strategy behind the time delay trigger . . . one has to ensure that it's impossible to open and deactivate the bomb during the forty-eight hours to Ground Zero. Savvy?'

I savvied. There was still one anomaly that worried me, though. I asked, 'So why risk tampering with it at all? Why not just sink her in thirty-plus fathoms and all go home?'

He looked at me sadly, even pityingly. 'Because, Captain, in the first instance ultra-sonic radio waves can be transmitted through water. It means your ship would remain a potential danger – no matter how remotely so – for the next hundred years, say. Or until such time as she finally disintegrates.'

I shivered a little. But it was only the cold room. I think.

'. . . And, as a logical sequence to that process, *if* the retaining bolts on the . . . ah . . . booby-trapped inspection cover did happen to rust away, then the cover would slip off, the manual trigger would still initiate the fusion process, and . . . you do see, don't you, Captain?'

Oh, I saw, all right! I saw a mile-wide column of super-heated Baltic water rising endlessly towards the clear blue sky. Except it was a sky which wouldn't dawn for maybe another century from now – and I, amongst others, would have been responsible for endowing tomorrow's unsuspecting world with that obscene legacy of twentieth-century war mania.

I said deliberately, 'Has it ever occurred to anybody that They may just resent us a little? The Soviets. Which could make them do some very unkind things? Like shoot bullets at you an' me and the rest of our crowd . . .?'

I watched sadistically for a reaction from the strange little soldier-scientist sitting opposite. 'What happens if they shoot *you* in the guts, Major? Who's going to defuse that bloody bomb then, eh?'

He didn't show any reaction at all. Apart from possibly a flicker of surprise. He just stared at me through his large horn-rimmed spectacles, and said conversationally, 'Oh, didn't you know? The reason for our little chat just now . . .?'

Of course I should have done. But I let him finish anyway.

'. . . I'm ordered to teach the technique to a security-cleared stand-in, Captain Cable. It means that if – by some chance – I'm killed, then *you* will be able to disarm the device yourself . . .'

The Royal Marine Commando Lieutenant was just a kid to look at. But that was only on first impressions. When he spoke, despite the deceptively casual public school drawl, I knew right away I was dealing with a master craftsman in weaponry. It made me feel a little more secure. I mean, if anyone had to get shot at then preferably it would be some poor squaddie with a red star on his hat.

I glanced uncomfortably round the basement armoury, noting the oiled metallic sheen of ready laid out small arms on the felt-covered table down the centre of the room. Somehow they appeared oddly alien in this highly sophisticated repository of British killing equipment.

'We're taking mostly Russian weapons, sir,' the Lieutenant murmured behind me, 'in case any of our chaps are unlucky . . . We don't want everything hallmarked with a Union Jack. It could prove a bit embarrassing at diplomatic levels.'

I knew what he meant. As far as the British Government were concerned OPERATION STAYSAIL didn't exist – and neither did any recognition of our status as combatants under the terms of the Geneva Convention. If we were caught it would be as stateless mercenaries, or – even worse – as Nazi sympathizers dressed in the non-uniform garb of espionage agents and revolutionaries. But that was the trouble with fighting a war when nobody else was – the people you were fighting for just didn't want to know. Not if you lost.

I picked up a sub-machine-gun and hefted it experimentally. The Lieutenant nodded. 'Soviet Avtomat Kalashnikov 7.62 millimetre assault rifle. Nice little job, too. All machined parts, no stamping like with the old Sten or the Yankee M3A1.'

It felt comfortable. If you liked guns. I sighted along it. 'Feels a bit like that Israeli model . . . the Uzi.'

He grinned. 'Better. More accurate. The average sub-machine-gun on single shot will produce a twelve to eighteen inch group at one hundred yards . . .'

'And this?'

'. . . every round'll smash a six inch plate!'

Or a man's face. I picked up an ammunition clip. 'These the shells?'

He nodded again. 'Normally the AK uses the standard Soviet M1943 cartridge – a straight crib from the old Jerry seven ninety-two *Kurz*, or "short" round. We're taking the old, full size 7.62 rimmed cartridges on this job.'

'. . . *Christ!*'

A man's face snarled at me from the shadows . . . I felt a

cold surge down my spine as I swung round with an empty, useless bloody gun to my hip . . . and then the distorted features dissolved into the flat plane of a standard Ministry of Defence snap target. The Lieutenant grinned sympathetically. 'They scare the hell out've me too, sir. But not as much as the real ones.'

I laid the sub-machine-gun back on the table feeling a little shaken. God, but my nerves were shot to ribbons before we even started out on this mission. Blast J.C.'s eyes! And McReadie's. *And* all the anonymous bloody planners who'd thought this scheme out to its conclusion . . .

The Commando OC walked slowly down the table, gesturing with the casual air of a thorough professional. He seemed a nice kid. I hoped he'd live to make a career of it. '. . . Soviet again, but a carbine this time – semi-automatic SKS . . . Simonov. Then that damn great cannon over there . . . It's an SGM. They call it the "Heavy Modernized Goryunov". It does duty as a battalion level machine-gun though they mount them on armoured personnel carriers too . . .'

I said, 'It looks as though you're going to start a war even if they don't, Lieutenant.'

He smiled wistfully. 'Only a little one, sir. Only a very little one.'

I glanced at my watch. Lunch time. Only I didn't want any lunch. But there was still that bloody Cable image to live up to. I hesitated at the door. 'Oh, by the way, Lieutenant . . . I didn't quite catch your name?'

He caressed a weapon which I vaguely recognized as a German Fallschirmjaeger Gewehr 42 automatic rifle. The youthful, impish face smiled softly. 'It's De'Ath, Captain . . . Aubrey De'Ath. With an apostrophe.'

I hoped it was only a name, and not an omen.

McReadie laid the entrails of his steak and kidney pudding open with the precise skill of a Royal Naval surgeon commander, then prodded his fork across the table at me.

'Did you know . . .' he asked with absorbed interest, '. . . that the effects of a Hiroshima-type twenty kiloton fission bomb are – according to the Major – similar to those of a six thousand piece artillery barrage firing . . . ah . . . one hundred thousand 105 millimetre shells within four minutes . . . ?'

I shoved my untouched plate away and glowered at him. 'So what, Commander? That thing aboard *Venturer*'s roughly two an' a half *thousand* times as big as the Hiroshima job . . . so where's the comparison?'

He loaded a forkful like a bulldozer driver on piece work. 'I don't know, Cable,' he shrugged, '. . . I don't think they ever thought it worthwhile calculating.'

I didn't want any apple crumble and custard either.

The man from the Department of Strategic Studies seemed to enjoy himself a great deal. But then, he wasn't actually going with us.

'The new Nazi Party, the *Wiedereinstellung*, are remarkably well organized, Captain. In the East German Democratic Republic, anyway.'

I resisted the temptation to point out that at least they were one step ahead of our mob for a start then, and asked, 'There are still only thirty thousand of them. How can they possibly deploy in any significant order of battle?'

He smiled superiorly. 'Tactics, Captain, are a little outside our mandate for today. However, the *Wiedereinstellung* set-up is based on the use of highly mobile, hit and run *Aufklarungsabteilung* . . . um . . . recce units, you understand? Rather like our old Long Range Desert Groups.'

'Mobile?'

'In terms of speed, yes. In terms of armour . . . no. Obviously they are entirely dependent on commandeered civilian transport for their strike units.'

I said coldly, 'You mean they'll use Volkswagens against tanks. With Luger pistols all round, of course.'

He shrugged. 'Even a nine millimetre pistol bullet can

still be a disruptive force, Captain. Especially if it hits you in the back of the head while you're facing the other way. And please don't forget – the Nazi uprising is purely a temporary guerrilla action. To disconcert and demoralize the Soviet and East German regular forces until such time as our Allied armoured spearheads can link up with them.'

I lit an Embassy Tipped without offering him one, and tried to look only half as disgusted as I felt. 'But they won't link up with the Allies, will they? Because there won't bloody well *be* any!'

He blinked placidly back. 'No, Captain. But isn't that a little outside our terms of reference, too? You know the form – "Ours not to reason why; Ours but to do . . ." '

. . . and die. Except that coldly supercilious, Whitehall warrior wasn't ever likely to do any of the dying. Not him. Not any of the chairborne tacticians who'd devised this lunatic operation. Not unless they tripped over their brollies and fell under the 5.25 back to the commuter belt . . .

I gave up thinking pleasant thoughts and sniffed irritably. 'Who's the new mini-Fuhrer, anyway? The Adolph Mark Two?'

He lit one of his own cigarettes and, for a brief moment, the smoke hid his eyes. When it cleared he was looking at me expressionlessly. 'His name's Geber . . . Horst Geber. And perhaps I should warn you, Captain – Herr Geber hates the British almost as much as he hates the Russians.'

I grunted, 'You make me feel better every minute. Is he a young Geber or an old Geber?'

'Born 1919. Frau Geber must have been quite a naughty lady in her way, Papa having been killed on the Western Front in '17. Or perhaps she was just a lonely woman . . . Anyway, young Geber did rather better than many of his contemporaries. He attended Hamburg University, did all the things a wealthy student did in those days . . .'

'Like?'

'Oh, winter sports in the Bavarian Alps. Protest meetings, *bier garten* revelries, climbing . . .'

'Mountains, or into other people's beds?'

He smiled dryly. 'Possibly a little of both, Captain. And in its broadest possible sense.'

I raised an eyebrow. 'Homosexual?'

A faint shrug. 'Horst Geber is rumoured to be a man of considerable and varied appetites.'

'And this Nazi affiliation? Got into that as a student, did he?'

'Joined the Party on August 3rd 1934 – the day after Hitler added the President's title to that of Chancellor, on Von Hindenburg's death . . . he was always something of a cautious man, Herr Geber.'

I leaned forward, fascinated by the potted biography of a man who apparently aspired to become a carbon copy of modern history's most revolting by-product. 'What kind of a war did he have?'

My informant shrugged again. 'Oddly enough, rather dull it would seem. He spent most of it in Paris as a *Stabscharführer* with the *Gegenspionage* section of the SS – in counter-intelligence. His duties brought him into close contact with French resistance techniques, of course, and that experience has proved invaluable to him in the current *Wiedereinstellung* set-up.'

'War crimes?'

'Another rather grey area in Geber's past, I'm afraid. There were several pointers to his having been involved in the torture of suspects but not enough evidence for a conviction – even by Soviet standards. He seems to have been very efficient at removing witnesses.'

I murmured, 'A lot of them were. He seems to be a pretty grey man all round, this Horst Geber.'

Another imperceptible shrug. 'It's a very good colour for a potential dictator . . .' He hesitated, chewing his lip. '. . . Would you accept a word of advice, Captain Cable?'

I spread my hands. 'I'll accept anything if it means living longer.'

'Then watch the *Wiedereinstellung* very carefully, do you

95

understand? And Geber in particular, if you meet him . . .
Because the night you attempt to steal *British Venturer* will
also be a night the new Nazis have been waiting for, and
for a very long time – it will be a night of terror, Captain. A
Night of the Long Knives!'

An involuntary shiver speared through me. 'Meaning?'

He shook his head. 'Many will die. Old men, women, even
children . . . they're *Nazis*, Captain. They spawn death by
their very way of life. Sometimes it becomes an unreasoning
madness with them . . . and your Staysail team will be in the
centre of the snake pit . . .'

I asked one more question before I left him. 'What does
he do now, this Horst Geber?'

The man from the Department of Strategic Studies looked
at me in a funny way. 'He's gone underground now, Captain,
but before he did he worked in the City of Ahldenstadt
itself . . .'

He stubbed out his cigarette delicately. '. . . the potential
Fuhrer of the Fourth Reich was employed in a profession
which, it is said, he enjoyed very much indeed . . . As a
slaughterman.'

'Excuse me, Admiral.' I asked in the nicest possible way,
'But what reasons did you give those Nazis to justify our
hijacking *Venturer* when, theoretically, we could walk
aboard an hour or so later with half the British and United
States' Armies as escorts? After the . . . ah . . . *landings* take
place.'

'Just the remote chance that the landings are a failure,
Cable,' he said, 'and the Soviets still hold Ahldenstadt . . .
We've told Geber half the truth – that *Venturer is* a special
ship, but only in the sense that she was actively spying when
arrested, and that we must insure against the loss of ir-
replacable electronic data she collated from Soviet Navy
signal patterns.'

I backed politely towards the door. 'Thank you, sir. I
couldn't help wondering . . . just in case Geber finds out

there never was a Task Force. *Before* we've sailed!'

Marine Colour Sergeant Lattice taught us how to kill a man, and with such surreptitious discretion that not even the victim himself could possibly have known he was dead.

In fact, Marine Colour Sergeant Lattice had a specialized technique for the manual extermination of anybody anywhere, depending only in its application on whether the enemy was engaged in a game of gin rummy, sentry duty, sexual intercourse or eating his dinner.

Or sleeping.

'It's not so easy as you might think, gentlemen. Killin' a bloke while he's havin' a kip . . .' Colour Sergeant Lattice explained to us morosely. '. . . Usually he sleeps all curled up in a little ball so's it's bloody near impossible to find a half-decent spot to stab him in. Right?'

McReadie glanced at me numbly and we both nodded, appalled at the awkwardness of people and at the difficulties they created for Marine Colour sergeants in pursuit of their legitimate profession.

Lattice looked even more frustrated. 'Then they nearly *always* sleep with their heads all tucked in . . . chin on chest, shoulders hunched up round their bloody ears . . . You can't get your hands anywhere for a good strangle. You jus' try it, sirs, an' see the difficulties.'

We shook our heads urgently. We believed Marine Colour Sergeant Lattice implicitly when it came to the problems of havin' a good strangle. Though there *was* J.C. up there . . .

The military tone was almost plaintive. '*How*, then, gentlemen, are we goin' to dispose of our target? In an orderly and completely discreet manner, of course.'

McReadie said tentatively, 'You could still get a bit of cheesewire round his neck, Colour Sergeant. Like a garrotte.'

I blinked at McReadie. I'd always known his imagination could rise to feats of improvization, but . . .

'Cheesewire, sir?' The Colour Sergeant echoed deprecatingly. 'No, I don't ever like to strangle no one with cheesewire. I only once used cheesewire, when I was just a squaddie – I wouldn't want to do it again.'

'Why not, Colour Sergeant?' I asked in shuddering anticipation. But I just had to know why cheesewire wasn't any good for people.

He looked sadly reflective. ' 'Cause his head toppled off've his shoulders, sir. Severed the spinal cord clean through, like a guillotine . . . an' a head can make a lot of noise, mind, when it falls to the deck. And *especially* if it still happens to be wearin' a steel helmet at the time.'

I muttered, 'Thank you, Colour Sergeant,' politely. And sat down.

The blue eyes regarded us with calculating detachment. 'No, gentlemen, there is only one way to dispose of your enemy while sleeping. You gotter creep up to him like a little mouse wearin' carpet slippers . . . You will rap sharply with your knuckles on his forehead, just above the bridge of his nose. His immediate reflex action is to draw his head away . . . which means he arches his neck in so doing . . .'

'Then what?' I whispered, feeling a bit peculiar.

He gazed at me with the critical sympathy of a master craftsman for his newly articled apprentice.

'. . . then you cut 'is bloody throat, of course, sir.'

I didn't bother going for tea. And the hell with the Cable image.

'By the way, McReadie,' I said, outside in the corridor. 'One thing I still haven't been told. How do we get to Ahldenstadt, anyway? By submarine?'

He shook his head. 'Not enough depth to operate in, old boy. It's got to be by plane.'

I swallowed nervously. That was my other nightmare. Flying. I tried to find a loophole. 'We can't, f'r Chrissake! They'd never miss us overflying Red air space. We'd be punched out of the sky before we crossed the coast.'

He shook his head again, cheerfully. 'It's all arranged, Cable. The RAF seem to have a . . . well, a similar sort of operation to us here in BMSNC. Where they run an air freight charter line which has been known to veer from the paths of legality on occasions. You can imagine the rest.'

'And they have clearance to cross the coast at Ahldenstadt?'

McReadie nodded, but I thought I detected a note of discomfort. I started to worry again – he spoke so bloody reassuringly. 'They have a permit to fly a cargo of machine parts from Norway into the East German commercial field near Prenzlau. Via Malmö, Sweden. It takes them virtually over Ahldenstadt itself.'

I frowned. '*Over*, yeah . . . but how do we land there? And how do we get off the plane unobserved when we do, McReadie?'

He inspected his toe caps very closely. 'They get engine trouble, old boy. It will force them down to around two thousand feet . . .'

I shouted, 'No! Definitely, positively *no*, McReadie!'

He continued remorselessly, '. . . then we jump, Cable. We all go out by parachute.'

I turned away with the nervous tic dragging at my mouth like a gaffed pike, then I swung back and stabbed an emphatic finger at him. 'Now hear me, McReadie, and hear me good. I am not . . . I repeat, *not*, jumping out of any aeroplane for anybody. Not even if it's on the ground without a ladder . . . Do – you – understand?'

McReadie said, 'Brev . . . Old pal . . .'

'Bugger you!' I yelled, really hating him for the first time in my life. 'I say again, McReadie – No! No . . .! NO . . .!'

They said the plane we were to drop from was an Argosy freighter. Personally it didn't look to me as if it could even get off the ground, never mind fly all the way to Germany. The only thing I wasn't interested in was its landing capability – I wasn't going to be aboard when it did, anyway.

McReadie stayed behind me all the time as we filed aboard. Maybe he thought I was going to make a break for it there and then, but he needn't have worried. The pills they'd given me had tranquillized me so much that – at this stage of the trip – I'd have jumped into East Germany wearing an umbrella and bowler hat instead of a parachute if they'd insisted.

Even the take-off didn't build up to my usual finger-digging climax. In fact it was only when I saw a bloke walking away from the cockpit and, to make conversation, said to McReadie, 'D'you think he's the pilot, Mac?' and *he'd* answered irritably, 'Well if he is, then get your chute on, Cable, seeing we've been in the air for the past six minutes!' that I realized we had. Taken off, I mean.

Then the effects of the pills started to wear off.

I peered round the hold of the plane, lit only by an eerie blue lamp instead of the extroverted, no-expense-spared brilliance of a civil airliner, and moodily brooded that this was the last time Cable ever flew Tourist Class. The whole of the forward end was stacked with wooden cases labelled 'Machine tools. This way up', and the care with which they'd been secured made it only too apparent that we – the passengers – were the second grade freight. But, then again, we weren't even going the whole way. And it was noisy, too, though I didn't mind that quite so much. At least it proved the engines were still running and we hadn't converted to gliding.

Or was that starboard one revving quite as smoothly as it should? While the deck did seem to slant a little to that side, as though the pilot was disorientated by a faulty instrument reading. And there was a row of rivets vibrating in the deckhead, shimmering little pools of blue reflection against the dull, cold gleam of the aircraft skin . . . But it *could* be the start of a collapse of the airframe. With the hull imploding around us, and the flailing buzz saw of the props slashing inwards while the severed, eviscerated shards of Argosy Golf Kilo Yankee Delta tore crazily away along the tunnel of our slipstream . . . and the bodies spinning and starfishing into black nothing . . .

I stared dully at the row of men sitting across from me. That big Marine Corporal at the end of the line, for instance. The one with his feet up on the packing cases, nonchalantly reading a paperback with the stolid, gum-chewing expression of an expendable bull *en route* to the abbatoire? Didn't the unimaginative bastard even suspect he might never have time to finish the chapter before those rivets pulled out and the whole bloody lot of us would be trying to sit on a cloud beside the aircrew . . . 'cause by then the plane would just be a hurtling, plummeting jigsaw puzzle of . . .

'Attention, please!'

I froze involuntarily until I realized it was only one of the Argosy crewmen shouting. He was standing at the forward end of the plane, holding easily to the starboard wire running fore and aft along the deckhead. Thirteen faces swivelled as one to listen expectantly.

'My name's Jollip, gen'lemen. Flight Sergeant Jollip, Harry. I'm your Air Quartermaster for tonight's little party, an' those two there . . .' He gestured towards another pair in flying overalls, '. . . they're your Dispatchers. They see you out the doors as smooth as the Royal butler would. *And* they make sure you got your chutes on when you go!'

Jollip, Harry, laughed heartily at his little bit of fun. I watched sourly – so maybe he was only trying to lighten the strain but, to me, he was still a bloody sadist. Anyone who pushed other people out of aeroplanes for a living just had to be.

Harry was talking again. 'Now the reg'lar Service blokes won't need any more than the green light but you other Naval gentlemen, well, you're going to need a hand to get your gear on and secured, so that's the first priority. If you'll just sit tight there and enjoy yourselves we'll come round an' get you all dressed up like dogs' dinners . . .'

Or sacrificial offerings. I stole a surreptitious glance around to see how the rest of the BMSNC contingent were getting on. McReadie, for instance, looked as placid as ever, but then he was a drivelling idiot anyway or he'd never have volunteered to come on this crazy, nightmare ride to God knows what.

One of the Dispatchers was already rigging young Twist out for the Big Drop and the way the Mate watched with such intense interest made me wonder if he wasn't just another from the McReadie mould. In fact, the only one who appeared as worried as me was the Chief Engineer and I felt a lot better, covertly watching him across the passage-way, when I noticed him toying with a packet of cigarettes in what was so obviously forced concentration.

Until the Cellophane wrapper tore off and he looked up, grinning happily, and said, 'These bloody packets . . . I never can find the damn tab to unwrap 'em.'

Inevitably the Dispatcher loomed over me and, as I couldn't think of one viable reason for aborting at this stage, I stood up and wearily held out my arms in an attitude of crucifixion. Doing that made me think of J.C. again, how much more satisfying it would be if he was jumping too . . .

I felt a tug at the last strap and the Dispatcher stood back looking critically pleased. 'Right, sir? All comfy enough?'

I nodded dumbly. There wasn't much point in doing anything else though I couldn't see how anyone but a deformed cripple could've felt at ease encased in a webbing cocoon with a cubical parachute pack like a foundation stone mounted fore and aft. Finally the Dispatcher produced a crash helmet thing and, with the flourish of a professional cabaret performer, crammed it on my head. 'Skid lid, sir. Just in case.'

Just in case . . . It was like that time so long ago, while we were waiting for the Soviet destroyers to move. Just in case! Except that this time I didn't even dare think about the possibilities. I tried to sit down but the chute on my back kept shoving me forward, off the seat, so in the end I settled for a sort of suspended limbo, angled on the points of heels, backside and helmet rear.

The plane droned on. And on. I started wanting to be sick again but, seeing I hadn't been able to eat a damn thing since I'd first heard about OPERATION STAYSAIL anyway, there didn't seem to be a lot of point in it.

I tried to wriggle my shoulderblades into a less cramped position but that wasn't any good so I pulled awkwardly at the webbing where it cut into my crotch. No improvement there either. The big Marine Corporal still ploughed through his paperback with about as much interest in his surroundings as I had in playing bridge right then. Even his parachute seemed to fit him like a built-in armchair and I started to hate the professionals with a bitter intensity while my fingers, desperate for something to occupy them, probed and prodded nervously at the big, square metal box under my reserve chute – that thing they called the 'Box, Web Straps, Quick Release'.

I started to think about those bloody rivets again, too.

It all seemed such a hell of a long and laborious way to go about dying . . .

'Prepare for action!'

Oh Jesus!

A great big hand squeezed my guts, snapping my eyelids closed for a terrified, anticipatory moment and, when I opened them again, I found that everyone else was on their feet and facing the rear of the plane.

My feet scrabbled on the aluminium deck as I clawed myself to the vertical, then I was swivelling aft along with the rest of the sheep. The Marine Commandos were already hooking the 'D' rings of their static lines on to the strops on the cables running fore and aft while the two Dispatchers attached the BMSNC crewmen's and the Ordnance Major's for us. As mine was secured I had a ridiculous feeling of complete and utter dependence. Like a baby still connected by its mother's umbilical cord – except that babies didn't jump two thousand feet out of the womb . . .

'Check your equipment!'

Air Quartermaster Jollip, Harry, was already in position, a fearsome troglodyte in a blue-washed cave as he stood easily aft with helmeted head misshapen under gigantic earphones over the bulk of his parachute. For a moment I thought he was going to jump too, then I noticed that he was secured to a ringbolt in the deck by a safety harness and thought that, whatever else Harry was, he was a clever man.

The Dispatchers, also wearing chutes, moved along the double line of men checking equipment in the prescribed manner. A pull here, a tug there and finishing with a sharp slap across the release box on the belly. Mine gave a reassuring but utterly wasted wink as he dealt with me.

Check the static line . . . Helmet properly strapped on . . . Reserve chute with its big, red emergency release clipped properly to my chest straps . . . The harness which was to suspend me over two thousand feet of nothing – check *that's* firmly secured . . . The Dispatcher slapped the gunmetal release plate sharply with the flat of his hand and . . .

. . . and the whole bloody indescribable lot fell off my shoulders on to the indescribable deck.

I didn't say anything. Largely because I couldn't speak.

The Dispatcher looked at me reproachfully. 'You been playing with yourself, 'aven't you, sir?'

I blinked back a flood of tears. I couldn't remember the last time I'd wanted to cry so much. Certainly not since I was a little boy, a happy, unafraid little boy who thought that a parachute was something you made with a dirty hankie and four bits of string tied to the corners.

My mentor the Dispatcher said again, 'You shouldn't have played with it – the Quick Release Box I mean, sir. That sort of milled disc on the front of it there. That's the first safety catch . . . Once you turn that then all you gotter do is slap the gubbins and . . . Presto! You're free of the gear.'

He hesitated. 'Mind you, sir. That's only for when you're down on the ground. If your chute's draggin' you along. I mean, you . . . ah . . . you aren't actually supposed to fall out've it half-way . . . but didn't they tell you all that at the para school, though?'

I whispered miserably, 'I haven't *been* to parachute school.'

He looked up from where he was gathering my equipment together for the second time. 'Ah . . .' he said, without the slightest trace of surprise, '. . . then you're a lot better off than if you had, sir. You see, to me parachutin's like the first time you have it off with a lady friend – you're better to get in there straight away than try an' read how to do it first, in a book . . .'

He strapped me up again, deftly, talking all the time. I knew he was only trying to buoy me up but, somehow, I felt the casual, chatty voice was relaxing me. Smoothing the edges of ragged nerves. I blinked at him gratefully. 'The only damn thing I know is that, if the main chute doesn't open, I yank on that big red ring and hope to Christ my other one does.'

The Dispatcher looked tremendously pleased. 'Well, there you are then, sir. An' what else *is* there to know once you got that taped? Look . . . I had one of the finicky types aboard here not so long ago – he was a Yank. They were doin' a first jump an' they'd been trained up to the bloody hilt . . . even to yell "Geronimo!" as they went through the door . . .'

Eagerly I filed that tactical gem away for future reference, though I didn't think it was quite so important as remembering to pull the big red ring. The Dispatcher continued, '. . . Now this bloke was last in the stick – dead nervous about forgettin' the smallest detail, he was – and they started jumping on the green light, one after another as smooth as a string of sausages. And each one, as he went out the door, hollers "Geronimooooooooooo!" at the top of his voice . . . until, eventually, they've all gone an' me an' the Air QM shuts the doors and goes forr'ad to the cockpit to report.'

I asked anxiously, 'Then what? What happened?'

He shook his head sorrowfully. 'Well, sir. We're up in the nose when – all of a sudden – there's this knock on the pilot's window, dead urgent . . . Scared the hell out've me, it did. Anyway, the FO slides the window open and, believe it or believe it not, there was that last Yank in the stick sort of clawin' and draggin' his way along the fuselage, hanging on like grim death against a two hundred knot slipstream . . . almost like his chute had caught up on the plane . . .'

He shuddered with the memory. I forgot where I was. I forgot the discomfort as the last straps pulled back into place. I even forgot those damned rivets while imagining the terror that trooper must have felt. 'What did the Yank say?' I muttered tensely.

The Dispatcher looked at me dead-pan. 'He said, sir . . . "F'r Chrissakes, Mac, but *what* was the name of that fuckin' Indian . . .?" '

And then it was time to go.

'Action stations!'

The Air Quartermaster was beckoning, both arms bent at the elbows and held vertically. I was aware of my line moving aft with a funny little shuffling, one-step walk and just followed numbly, holding on to my static line strop as if it were the only tangible thing in a suddenly unstable world.

Without warning the side jump doors slid open and the interior of the plane was immediately transformed into a whirling, shrieking hell of noise. I closed my eyes, starting to tremble all over as the beating of the engines enveloped me with an almost physical impact. Something gave me a violent prod in the back and I realized it was McReadie, still watching warily for a prospective abort. I turned and he gestured aft so I just blinked accusingly at him, carried on shuffling, and wished it was all over.

We were jumping in what they called a 'Sim Six' – two sticks simultaneously, from port and starboard doors. In the port stick we had De'Ath, the Marine Commando Lieutenant, as number one, then two more weapon-decorated Marines, then me and McReadie with Marine Colour

Sergeant Lattice to bring up the rear. I just had time to notice Major Gray, young Twist and the Chief filing grimly and stubbornly along the other side of the fuselage before McReadie shouted 'Red Light!' in my ear and even I knew that we were exactly two minutes from the drop.

A trickle of cold sweat ran down the side of my face and I craned my head to rub it against my sleeve. I don't think I've ever been so frightened in my life as I was then, with the roar of the engines rebounding around the aluminium skin of the Argosy, and the probing hurricane of wind lifting and whirlpooling dust and stray litter from every corner of the plane.

I hardly gave a thought to the fact that, had I been able to look down, then probably at that very second in time I would have been able to see the silver sheen of the Baltic meeting the curving coastline of the so-called German Democratic Republic. And the lights of a city called Ahldenstadt, with a million sleeping people who might be dead tomorrow if McReadie and Twist and the Chief and I didn't succeed tonight.

Maybe sixty seconds to go.

Oh God, but the *noise* . . . And I'm so bloody, bloody scared I just want to fling myself down in a corner and curl up in a tight, protected little ball. And those Goddamned Marines all ready to go with their practised military jumping stance . . . Body erect, one leg forward and slightly bent with the other ready braced for the launch. Arms folded firmly across chest . . . Multi-coloured now with the blue fuselage light blending in with the red light over the door . . .

I mean *green* light!

Oh *Jesus!*

The Dispatcher slapped Number One sharply. 'Green on . . . *GO!*'

A frozen glimpse of a mouth wide and shouting, with the battering gale vibrating and shrieking, tugging greedily at overall folds, then he was gone, headfirst, out into the blackness of the night.

And Two. And Three . . . And I'm moving towards the gaping door on leaden, dragging feet with the sweat pouring free down my face and my heart pumping in great, shuddering spasms until the Dispatcher swings me round towards the hole in the wall. An impression of warily-watching but sympathy-filled eyes, then his mouth against my ear, 'Go, sir . . . Jus' let yourself go.'

But I couldn't. Not out there. Not out into that rushing, gaping emptiness. I was bracing involuntarily against the door, forcing myself back into the plane. God, but it was suddenly so safe and secure, now. And I didn't care what they did to me . . . I didn't even care about those bloody rivets, not any more. Just let me stay and curl up and cry away my horror. Please? *Please* . . .

I half turned in the doorway and sobbed, 'Please no, McReadie.'

Just before his boot came up and quite deliberately shunted against my midriff. And I was screaming and scrabbling for a firmer handhold because I knew then he was going to kill me . . . while the Dispatcher lunged forward urgently, bellowing, '*No*, sir! Else he'll go out all twisted f'r a bloody candle . . .'

Then my compo-soled boot skidded into space, and I felt my nails breaking away from the cold alloy of the fuselage, and the blue square of light with the men frozen into horrified statues rose away up into the sky. And I thought, 'That's funny – about the plane climbing like that.'

Until I realized it wasn't the plane climbing at all, but that it was *me* falling out've the bastard . . .

They say that, when someone lapses into the hysterical frenzy that I was in during those terror condensed moments before the drop, that the only action to take is to slap them around a little. To shock them into normality. And somehow that's just what happened to me, except I was slammed around in a two hundred knot wind tunnel instead.

The trouble was that I'd gone out of the door like a bundle

of dirty washing instead of in a compact, streamlined dive. I can't remember much about the first ten lifetimes of falling, other than that I had legs protruding where there shouldn't have been any, and my arms were flailing and semaphoring uncontrollably as I tumbled head over heels with all the grace of a wind-blown paper bag.

The turbulence was incredible. It dragged me out, spun me over and over, swung me round in a gigantic, crazy ariel pirouette then, with infinite contempt, threw me a thousand miles away into the black turntable void. Yet somehow, after all the terror and the agony and the tormented anticipation, I suddenly became coldly and resignedly aware. I felt myself falling – *saw* myself falling – with the long umbilical cord of the static line trailing behind, and a little voice in my head started screaming, 'Get your arms up, Cable! Get your arms up so's that webbing can't coil around your neck or it'll tear your bloody head off . . .'

Then there was a surprisingly delicate little tug at my back and I knew my chute was incredibly streaming out astern of me, and I felt the forces of gravity taking over from the displaced air of the Argosy's passing, and it became very quiet with only the drone of synchronized aero-engines whispering a long way above.

And I thought with deep, unbelievably sweet satisfaction, 'Now *this* is a bit of all right, Cable boy. A proper bit've all right . . .'

In fact it wasn't until I'd passed two dangling, swaying men in the night – and watched with critical fascination as a third fluted, rippling canopy hurtled up towards me at thirty feet per second – that I finally realized that the Dispatcher had been right, and McReadie had been wrong . . .

. . . because my chute hadn't opened after all!

On reflection, I suppose I'm being unfair to say it hadn't opened, because it had. Only it wasn't much use to me anyway because, as I craned my head back trying desperately to distinguish solid form from the lighter velvet of the night sky, I found that all I could see was a sort of end elevation of a gigantic salami sausage with the top part waggling and spiralling furiously maybe twenty feet above me.

I had a fleeting vision of the Dispatcher's shocked features before I fell, and his open mouth yelling at McReadie, '*No*, sir! Else he'll go out all twisted f'r a bloody candle . . .!'

I'd heard them use the phrase before, it was a para-trooper's nightmare – they called it a 'Roman Candle', and it happened when your rigging lines wrapped around each other, round and round again, until the belly of the chute was drawn and extended, and the air couldn't slam it open to break your fall.

Twisted. Like mine was.

Someone was screaming, too. Some panic-stricken, self-centred bastard was screaming in a long, high-pitched wail of unutterable sadness. Screaming 'Noooooooooooo . . .' all the time, and it made me very angry indeed. Until I realized the screaming was mine, and that the third parachutist was a long way above me. And that I was going to die horribly in a very few seconds with my shin bones driven up into my chest cavity, and my shattered frame forming a compacted, skeletal bier for staring, shocked eyes in a grounded skull . . .

I closed them and tried to forget.

To *forget*?

Eyes open again, frantically. A memory from long ago . . . In a dive in Singapore . . . or was it Batavia . . .? Ahhh, the *hell* with it! A memory of a beer-swilling, outrageously drunken British Army para sergeant sneering blearily and contemptuously at a flock of fresh-faced, beardless kids. Mocking them, and spitting, 'Mummy's boys! Gutless bloody wonders . . . I seen lots like you before – all buried up to their fuggin' ears in self-dug graves . . . All smashed inter bloody plasma 'cause they was too scared even to remember to pull their emergency packs . . .'

I clawed for the red plastic-covered 'D' ring on my breast. And yanked.

And started to cry unashamedly as the cold reserve silk flailed my face while it snaked quite ridiculously into a beautiful, climbing column.

But I didn't mind. Crying, I mean. Because I'd wanted to for quite a long time.

I don't remember much more about that mad, mad drop. Other than when I'd finally landed, still feeling as though I'd been flung from the top of a medium-sized cliff. But then, the reserve chute had been a lot smaller, and I *was* still alive.

I think.

I lay flat on my back and stared up at the sky, and just had time to note a string of black, swaying discs a long way above me – twelve of them, in fact – and grin stupidly as I giggled, 'I won, you lazy, idle, professional heroes. Cable's won the bloody race 'cause he's first down . . .'

Then my parachute ballooned enormously astern of me as a stray cat's-paw of wind filled it, while my harness slammed tight against my shoulders and I was off again, dragging helplessly and without a shred of dignity, at enormous speed across what seemed to be a ploughed field but felt more like being towed by a Grand Prix racer over a corrugated tin roof.

Until a tree, or a stone wall or a damn great farmhouse jumped up in the air and hit me over the back of the skid lid and I blacked out.

But even that was nice. Not to have to be afraid any more.

Part Two

Six

'Masthead . . .'

The voice came from a long way away. Guttural and urgent, it seemed to be a pretty silly thing to say, what with the ship rolling and pitching like this, and me only half awake in my bunk . . . Then I opened my eyes with the sudden shock of realization. And found the ship wasn't rolling at all because I wasn't *on* a ship, and that my bunk was really the soft, sweet-smelling grass cushioning the base of a hard stone dyke.

And the voice repeated, even more urgently, 'Masthead!' while the necessity for some form of reply was given considerable priority by the unmistakable snick of a sub-machine-gun bolt easing out of its safety recess.

I tried to forget the blinding ache at the back of my skull and muttered, '. . . Lookout.' And prayed to God I'd given the correct answer to the challenge. Then strong hands grasped me under the arms and lifted me to what were, presumably, my feet, but felt more like great unstable splodges of jelly.

No one shot me though, which seemed to confirm that 'Masthead Lookout' had indeed been the correct identification format. It also told me that, at last, I was facing a small section of Horst Geber's embryonic Nazi Phoenix – the *Wiedereinstellung*.

It also struck me that the shooting Cable bit might only be temporarily delayed, too. Until the crowd waving guns in front of me gradually realized they'd been conned into making a bigger mistake than Hitler did when *he* declared war on Russia the last time. But that was for later, right now

I was more concerned about bullets with little red stars on them.

Someone stepped forward from the shadowy group, moonlight glinting on the colander of an air-cooled gun barrel. Then an arm shot stiffly skywards and I was staring in undisguised astonishment at the spectacle of a Nazi salute being offered to me, Brevet Cable, nautical parachutist and invader extraordinary.

I didn't return it. Not even the British way. I just nodded curtly and hoped that McReadie would turn up soon. The man before me said briskly, 'Paulus Kleiber . . . *Hauptmann*. And you are . . .?'

I returned, 'Cable. Brevet Cable . . . Captain.'

'From the British Army, *Herr Hauptmann*?'

My head waggled emphatically. 'British Merchant Navy. I'm a *Kapitän*, not a *Hauptmann* . . . You found the rest of my crowd yet, have you?'

The man called Kleiber shrugged. 'We will meet up with them soon. The correct dropping zone is a few hundred metres to the south. It was only chance which brought you down here among us, *Kapitän* . . .' I saw his eyes flicker to the useless roll of my main parachute as it trailed out astern of me like a great fat tail, '. . . or perhaps, as a seaman, you are being saved to *ertränken* . . . to drown, ja?'

They all had a bloody good dutiful laugh then but I didn't really mind – it also proved to me that most of them spoke English, which meant we'd have to watch what we said while little Nazi ears were around. The *Hauptmann* slapped the butt of his gun and the laughing stopped as if he'd thrown a switch. He turned back to me. 'We will go now, if you are ready.'

I wished that I had a gun to slap around too, but I'd given mine to Marine Colour Sergeant Lattice for delivery to the ground. Jumping had been enough of a problem for Cable without having to carry a full cargo as well.

I said, 'O.K.,' and promptly fell over my chute webs.

They didn't laugh this time. Maybe they were beginning

to worry a little about what kind of idiots the British had donated to help launch the glorious Fourth Reich Kleiber just stepped forward and slapped my release box coldly. 'Your *haltegurt*, *Kapitän Cable*. Your parachute harness. You will leave it here for us to conceal. Now, please hurry!'

We moved off in single file. I could dimly see that there were eight men in Kleiber's section, all dressed in a kind of black denim overall and armed with an assortment of automatic weapons which they apparently handled with ease. I just hoped they knew how to use them when it came to the crunch.

I looked at my watch in the blackness. The green luminous fingers pointed to 11.12 p.m. We had just under six hours to hijack *Venturer* – if we ever got that far in the first place . . . I shivered, it was getting near the time when all sensible people go to sleep. When villains take to their nocturnal pursuits. The time when very sick people die, and even some healthy but foolish ones . . .

The trees pointed towards the sky like dead men's fingers, with the only sounds in the whispering, probing breeze and in the gurgle of far-off water. Over to my left I could see an orange glow in the night – the lights of the City of Ahldenstadt. Christ, but I hoped we'd find McReadie soon! And all those great big, reassuringly aggressive Marine Commandos . . .

'Masthead.'

The column froze. It had only been a whisper but it held a note of indefinable menace. The kind which creeps into a man's voice when he has a target lined up and only needs the slightest excuse to squeeze the trigger. Kleiber never moved a muscle, he just breathed harshly, '. . . Lookout.'

I didn't move either. I even stopped the breathing part for the few seconds it took for young De'Ath to step warily forward, the muzzle of that evil Fallschirmjaeger still pointing obliquely down the line at belt-buckle level. Then he recognized me and I caught the flash of teeth in the darkness.

117

'Captain Cable, sir,' he said. 'Lord but you were abso-bloody-lutely fantastic. Congratulations.'

Then someone moved behind him and I saw it was McReadie, but I didn't let him see how pleased I was. I just gritted, 'I jump that way all the bloody time, Lieutenant. All it needs is a good kick in the guts from an old friend.'

McReadie grinned too, like an idiot. 'You're down, aren't you, mate?' he said indifferently.

I glared at him. 'Yeah. But doing it your way I should've finished up a different bloody shape, McReadie . . . Like a table mat with a head.'

Hauptmann Kleiber clicked rubber heels together, looking a bit lost, and snapped, 'Kleiber. *Hauptmann* . . . detached from *Wiedereinstellung Armee-Oberkommando*. Welcome to East Germany.'

De'Ath looked dryly at the inverted Nazi arm and returned the salute gravely. 'Lieutenant Aubrey De'Ath, Royal Marines. And this is Commander McReadie, Royal Navy.'

McReadie gazed at the *Hauptmann* with ill-concealed dislike. 'And as I don't have my cap on perhaps you won't mind if we cut out the formalities, *Herr* Kleiber? *Nicht formsache*, eh? *Nicht salutieren.*'

The German fondled the stock of his AK assault rifle. 'Actually I speak very good English, *Fregatten-Kapitän* McReadie. I had an excellent opportunity to learn the language as a prisoner of war. In a British *stalag*.'

'Then you were lucky, weren't you?' McReadie replied with icy precision. 'In a Russian prison camp you would only have had time to learn to stay alive . . .'

We started walking. All mates together.

In a hostile, uneasy kind of way.

It was really only when we came to a main road that I first realized the outrageousness of our position. It had started to rain and I just lay there in the wet grass inside the tree line, and hugged my 7.62 mm AK like a kiddy's Teddy bear, and watched the cars sweep by, ducking every time the amber caress of the headlights flickered across our blackened, sweat-streaked faces.

And thought how unbelievable it would be to imagine a group of armed Russian parachutists doing exactly the same thing alongside the A30 into Exeter, or the A165 just outside Hull. Except that they would be shooting at incredulous men from the Green Howards or the Royal Scots Greys, or the Lancashire County Constabulary in a very few minutes from now.

A movement beside me and I twisted round with nerve ends jangling like the back legs of a grasshopper. The impassive features of Paulus Kleiber, revolutionary-elect, stared at me from the darkness.

He gestured to his watch. 'Eleven-forty-four, *Kapitän*. In sixteen minutes the . . . what do you say ? . . . the balloon will shoot up. The *abfarts* signal – the starting signal – will be an attack on the main Soviet *infanterie-kaserne*, you understand?'

'You mean the barracks? Yeah, but what about the rest of the local defences, Captain? And the armoured elements who're going to be out and about just as soon as the shooting starts?'

He smiled without any humour at all. 'The tanks we will try to avoid. The other military posts are already attended to, also the *Vopos* and *Polizie* centres.'

A headlight flashed across my eyes, leaving little yellow spots ganging in the blackness. I said, '*Vopos?*'

He spat. 'Secret Police, you would call them. They are bad . . .' He shrugged suddenly and the teeth bared wolfishly, '. . . but we will attend to them, *ja*? We will be attending to many things tonight, *Herr Kapitän*.'

The Night of the Long Knives! And was there really any difference between *Vopos* and *Gestapo*? I shivered again and drew away fractionally from the heat of his body. He shouldn't be warm, not Kleiber. Not him or any of his mates. They should all feel cold, the soulless, deathly cold of

119

the living corpses that they were. Even the chill metal barrel of my Avtomat Kalashnikov felt more homely, more welcoming . . .

Someone wriggled up beside us and the soft voice of Lieutenant De'Ath broke the uncomfortable silence. 'How long do we lie here, *Hauptmann*? According to my briefing we have quite a march ahead of us, even to the outskirts . . .'

'*Achtung!*'

Kleiber suddenly held up a warning hand and part-rolled to one side, listening intently. I blinked into the darkness and gripped the AK even tighter, but all I could hear was the gentle whisper of the leaves above and, faintly, the roar of approaching diesel engines from the west.

The Nazi spoke low and urgently to two of his section. They nodded and, rising noiselessly, doubled off into the night with guns tucked well into black-overalled hips. Kleiber turned to us and smiled in a pleased sort of way. 'The walking is finished. Your transport is here, gentlemen . . . my men have gone a few metres up the road to signal. You will gather your equipment, if you please.'

It was the first time I'd been grateful to anyone for anything that night.

There were two canvas-canopied lorries. They drew into the verge directly opposite and we moved over, the Marines carrying their heavy demolition gear with the casual ease of very fit men. I caught a brief flash of that voracious-looking Goryunov heavy machine-gun being mounted on its tripod over the tailboard of the second lorry, then McReadie dug me in the back and snapped, 'Up, f'r Chrissake, Cable! We only have eleven minutes to catch up with the war.'

I scrambled aboard and sat down miserably between two king-sized man-packs of TNT. The literary-minded Marine Corporal I'd watched so bitterly in the plane trod on my hand with compo-soled boots that felt like power presses, said, 'Sorry, sir,' in a West Country dialect which still didn't conceal the fact that he wasn't really sorry at all, then squatted unconcernedly on enough high explosive to blow him, me, his boots *and* the rest of the bloody convoy all the way to Ahldenstadt without even touching the ground.

Bloody Marines. Bloody mud, wet grass an' walking! I closed my eyes as the lorry ground off with a jerk, and just wished I was back in my own element – on a ship's bridge, with the clean blue sea below and the seabirds wheeling and shrieking through the sheer excitement of an ocean's promise. This creeping through the night like a predatory animal was for another kind of man, a land-bound man with platinum wires for nerves and stainless steel tubes for a belly.

Hauling out a pack of Capstan Full Strength I spun the wheel of my lighter. Over the tailboard of the truck the stars looked very bright now, and it had stopped raining, which was something. I dragged down a satisfying gout of smoke and started to relax a little. Just maybe things could work out after all? Just maybe . . .

A military voice from the rear yelled, 'Put that fucking light out!'

But I should have known. I mean, a sailorman without a ship? It makes him just another bloody private.

The killing started precisely at midnight.

Immediately we ground to a halt the German resistance men were all around the vehicles, stripping their canvas covers off until the frames were left rearing above me like the bones of some skeletal night monster. Blinking cautiously around I saw we were now in a narrow, deserted back street with the half-timbered and high, gabled fronts of silent, sleeping houses on both sides.

Colour Sergeant Lattice climbed lightly over the tail of my truck and moved towards me. I noticed him wink briefly in the yellow street lighting then, gesturing to the big Marine Corporal, they deftly set up a second tripod-mounted general purpose machine-gun over the cab of the lorry itself. I started to tremble a little with sick anticipation – the act seemed to emphasize that we were now very near to the point of no return.

Except I knew I'd already passed it a long time ago. The minute I'd taken *British Venturer* abeam of the Falsterborev Light, and into the Baltic Sea.

'*Kapitän.*'

I leaned over the side of the truck and met *Hauptmann* Kleiber's eye. He pointed towards the end of the street. 'Down there is the Ahldenstadt *Technische Hochschule*. I think you would say, "Technical College". And around the corner there is the *Hagedornestrasse Polizie* post . . . we must deal with it before we continue.'

I said, 'Then what?'

He grinned tightly. 'Then, *Kapitän*, we have a further eight kilometres to the dock where your ship is lying. I suggest you hold very tight, *ja?*'

I nodded '*Ja!*' with emphasis while he glanced at his watch. A shadowy movement from the street corner caught my eye and I brought the AK round automatically. Kleiber held up his hand warningly. 'They are my men, *Kapitan*. They are preparing for the signal.'

The *Wiedereinstellung* group were too far away from me to make out detail, but the way they had deployed on that corner had a sinister, frightening promise to it. I felt a trickle of sweat run down the side of my face while, unexpectedly and from a long way away, a car horn blew irritably, bringing a flicker of temporary normality into our crazy, impossible world. Then the car horn stopped blaring and the silence clamped down again like a blanket. Or was it a shroud?

The waiting figures around the trucks stood motionless. My watch said one one five niner and thirty seconds . . . Oh, please God. Let me get through this lot tonight. Please . . .

An English voice whispering to the Corporal above me – the Colour Sergeant's. 'Easy, lad. An' remember . . . military targets only, mind. No knockin' off no civvies.'

Fifteen seconds to go.

The men at the end of the alley knelt like black paper cut-outs against the bright street lighting ahead of them.

That Police post? Just exactly where was it? And what about the unsuspecting coppers who were manning it? What happens to them when they come piling out into the glare of the main street . . .?

It was very, very quiet. Like the inside of a deaf mute's grave.

. . . D minus one second.

Oh, *Jesus*!

Some silly bastard started throwing coffee beans on to a drum skin beside the truck. Then I realized it wasn't coffee beans at all but the rattle of small arms fire, and that it came from a long way away. There was a deeper, reverberating boom and a flash lit up the night sky, throwing red and black shadows momentarily across the fronts of the houses to my left. Then another flash. And another . . .

. . . and the Fourth Reich was born. By violence out of hatred. Oh Christ, but I wanted to be sick again.

Kleiber moved fast. I saw him swing himself up on to the running board below me and his arm slash down. Even the harsh, barely controlled excitement in his voice couldn't conceal the fanatical pride he was feeling at that moment.

'*Anlasser! Anlasser sogleich . . .!*'

The truck engines roared into life. The throb bounced around the enclosing walls in almost hysterical anticipation. It was All Systems Go for the great, bloody revolution. *Götterdämmerung*, Nineteen Seventies style . . . *Deutschland über alles* all over again . . .

. . . except they didn't have a hope this time around. Not even a prayer.

I noticed the men from the Police post then. Little black silhouettes, running bewilderedly across the floodlit 'T'-junction and not really knowing why they were running, or where to. Until the *Wiedereinstellung* group opened up on them from point blank range, and I watched the orange stabs of flame from the traversing machine-gun, with the tracers ricocheting crazily from the wet, glistening cobbles. And the shop windows opposite collapsing into pretty, twinkling cascades of reflected colour . . .

. . . while the running men went down in a legless heap, skidding and tumbling across their very own patch of pavement like unstuffed Teddy bears. Except it wasn't sawdust and cotton waste I could see varnishing the gutters.

Then *Hauptmann* Kleiber roared, '*Vorwärts!*' and the gearbox engaged with a crash of protest, and we slammed away towards the lights with a jerk which brought every movable item of gear in the truck crashing backwards, including me. And when I'd picked myself up I found we'd left the silent, sleeping houses behind and were racing for the waiting ambushers and the bright, exposing glare of the main street, and the sprawling, untidy men we'd just killed.

Something big went up in a flash of fire which lit the sky for miles. I caught sight of Colour Sergeant Lattice standing, legs straddled to the sway of the lorry and sub-machine-gun angled to cover the approaching corner. He grinned an unholy grin and shouted, 'Sounded like an ammo dump, sir. Proper noisy bastards is Jerries!'

I smiled weakly back and wished to God I really had bought that bloody farm I'd been promising myself ever since McReadie had landed me in that last hopeless mess aboard the *Ayacucho City*. Then I remembered McReadie himself and stared anxiously back to where the second truck bounced in our wake. Please God, don't let anything happen to McReadie either. Or to young Twist, or the Chief. Or to hydrogen bomb expert, Major Gray. In fact, *especially* not to hydrogen bomb expert Major Gray . . .

We skidded to an abrupt halt and I leaned over to haul one of the *Wiedereinstellung* machine-gunners into the lorry. I noticed he was only a kid when I saw him close up, with his eyes bright as stars against the black-smeared face, and the hysterical excitement of the kill emanating from him like a tangible musk.

Until – quite ridiculously – the kid's shoulderblade exploded into a jagged, shapeless mess, and the young face looked suddenly odd as the top of his skull disappeared. And he fell away from my shocked, nerveless hands at the very second that Marine Colour Sergeant Lattice bellowed, '*Window*, Corporal! Two-o-clock high . . .'

The heavy machine-gun mounted on the cab started slamming against the West Country Corporal's shoulder just as I caught sight of the uniformed man firing at us from the first-floor windows of the *Hagedornestrasse* Police Station.

Then the entire window frame fell out into the street in a haze of concrete splinters, and the man behind it disappeared on the end of a stream of tracer shells which temporarily linked him to us in the most intimate sort of way.

And Lattice shouted, 'Cease firing!' because we had to save our ammunition and there weren't any windows left anyway. Or policemen.

The Corporal said, 'I never actually killed a bloke before,' in a rather surprised but dubious way, then we were off again with the OPERATION STAYSAIL teamsters clinging on like grim death and the spreadeagled, undignified corpse of an idealistic kid with half a head fading astern in the darkness.

I'd never been in a five ton truck taking corners on two wheels until then. One brief glimpse of McReadie's vehicle apparently broadsiding crazily across the tailboard of our own do-it-yourself *Blitzkrieg* kit, then we were into the bend with the overhead sodium lamps flashing aft above my head like tracer fire, and Brevet Cable was on his way down to the deck for a second time.

And by the time I'd got myself reorientated the house lights were coming on again in Ahldenstadt. Presumably every citizen and his *Frau* had leapt out of bed and hit the switch at the first blast of fire from the streets. Now they were peering nervously from behind fractionally parted curtains at the hurtling advance of Kleiber's assault group, or perhaps they still remembered that curiosity wasn't encouraged from three decades ago and just crawled back to the security of the sheets for the first time since the *Gestapo* handed their truncheons over to the Allies. Or had the

Vopos kept the good old Big Brother tradition going meanwhile?

But maybe just a few of them – the ones who remembered Germany before the blacks and the greys took over – maybe they started hunting around under the floorboards or in the attic for that old *Landsturm* Luger, or shotgun, or grenade . . . Angry, proud little people had done it once before, a long time back on 23 October 1956. In a place called Budapest, Hungary.

We got over two hundred yards down the *Hagedorne-strasse* before the elderly man with the Nazi armband and the frantically waving arms ran out in front of us. Below me, on the running board, Kleiber leaned in towards the driver. '*Aufenthalt . . . Schnell!*'

He hit the road at a run before we'd even stopped and I heard the man shout, '*Panzerwagen . . .!*' Then Kleiber gesticulated urgently and we started piling out of the trucks at a fast trot. He ran up to me as I dropped to the deck and I saw the tense excitement burning in his eyes.

'Armoured car, *Herr Kapitän*! We can go no further until it has been dealt with.'

Lieutenant De'Ath came round the back of the second lorry. 'Colour Sergeant Lattice.'

'*Sah.*'

'GPMG section, please. On the double!'

Another authoritarian voice, McReadie's this time. 'Hit those bloody headlights up front.'

The *Hauptmann* hesitated. I could see he wasn't too keen on the British Combined Ops team taking over and stealing the *Wiedereinstellung* embryonic thunder, then he abruptly swung round to his driver and spoke sharply. The headlight beams died immediately and it grew very quiet apart from the rattle of sporadic small arms fire from the eastern edge of the city.

A movement on my right and I was gazing into McReadie's eyes. He grinned tightly and said, 'All right?'

I shrugged and tried to look as if it was. He shivered a

little and pulled the collar of his coat up around his ears while we both stared hard down the glistening street with its deserted doorways and its silent, curtained windows.

'It's a bastard,' McReadie murmured softly. 'Just waiting for them to come and have a crack at you like this.'

I didn't answer. As far as I was concerned it had been a bastard from the minute I'd walked into J.C.'s office all that time ago, before I'd ever heard about megalomaniac mini-revolutionaries and bloody mad maritime hijack schemes. And booby-trapped thermo-nuclear bombs that you couldn't even tell were there. Not until they went off . . .

The headlights came slowly round the corner about three hundred yards away. The elderly German with the armband kneeling beside Kleiber hawked contemptuously and spat. *'Sowjet dünger!'* And that didn't need any translation, not even for me.

McReadie muttered, 'They're coming this way,' as the geometric silhouette behind the headlights settled on a whispering, steady course towards us, keeping well to the centre of the street. Even through the glare I could distinguish the turret swivelling, gun barrel searching hungrily for a target of opportunity. Like us. I closed my eyes and started praying that Lattice was as good at the practice of killing as he was at the theory – either with or without a bit o' bloody cheesewire.

Young De'Ath called softly, 'Down, everybody . . . *Sich niederlegen.'*

I was damned glad he'd finally said it. Personally I'd been fighting the temptation to take cover ever since we'd dismounted. Wriggling in behind the dubious safety of the truck's nearside wheel I peered through the shadows in search of the Commando section who'd moved forward, but I couldn't see a damned thing – apart from an approaching armoured car with a Soviet star on it which was going to try and kill me in maybe another two minutes.

Fire, f'r Chris . . . Go on! *Fire*, you idle bastards!

Seventy-five yards.

Please fire.

Seventy . . . I heard the metallic snick of McReadie's safety selector catch sliding off. 'Stuff you, McReadie . . .' I thought savagely. '. . . You an' your Thin Red Line ideals, an' your flamin' "Don't fire 'til you see the whites of their eyes, chaps" . . .' Well *I* can see the whole rotten eyeball now, mate, an' I'm buggered if it's going to be Cable's blood making that thin red British line of your . . .'

Fifty yards. 'Oh Jeeeeees *US*!'

And . . . it's *stopped*.

I saw the splash of sweat on the butt of my AK, then I was dragging it into my shoulder with my finger groping for the trigger. They were all mad, the whole crazy lot of them. Hiding like a bunch of kids playing soldiers in a make-believe world where a bush is a castle and a patch of corn becomes an impenetrable, armoured façade . . . McReadie's hand came up and slammed the muzzle of my gun down angrily.

I was glad after. He probably saved my life.

They'd seen us. The turret vectoring desperately now, swinging on to the blacked-out trucks. A whine as the armoured car's engine revved and he started to back away nervously, trying to close the angle of deflection even quicker . . . Slam! Slam! Slam! Slam! . . .! Somebody – De'Ath? – opening up at the headlights with a deliberate, single shot aim, and glass shattering and tinkling on the wet tarmac while the yellow beams sliced off into blackness.

A hunched figure, doubling low and suddenly clear in the absence of glare. Something rolling and bouncing under the high clearance between the huge rubber tyres . . . Then all hell let loose as the Commando machine-gun opened up at the same time as the Russian's turret weapons, and I was scrabbling at the mud-caked underbelly of the truck above me while the tracers whined and shrieked towards us, ricocheting hysterically on a closing course of flying splinters.

And McReadie firing just in front of my face, with the hot

exhaust gases from his ejector port choking and burning. But I could still see the other gun – Lattice's gun – pouring a cascade of shells into the soft-skinned after end of the car . . .

. . . until the thing they'd rolled under her exploded, and she blew up with such force that the whole carcase lifted twenty feet off the road and spat a pink piece of a man from her turret, then the mess of steel sort of tipped over sideways while still airborne and crashed back into a mad movies sequence of bouncing, spinning wheels and flying metal plates and catherine wheel fragments.

While we just hugged the road in our individual terrors, and felt the trucks above us groan and rock on tortured, blast-torn springs. Then the twisted tin coffin glowed an incandescent red with the skin of it erupting into showers of white hot sparks as the ammunition in her started to detonate, and I felt a vague surge of nausea. But it wasn't half as overpowering as the huge, blossoming glow of relief that warmed my belly to realize it wasn't Brevet Cable cremating in there.

Then I remembered we still had a hell of a long way to go before the docks, and that the Soviets would be getting more and more organized all the time, so I stopped feeling relieved and just stayed sick.

The Colour Sergeant's MG section came doubling back up the street, carrying the gun. I caught a glimpse of their faces as they moved past. They weren't pleased or elated, or even sad. They were just the impassive, disciplined expressions of professionals doing a job of work, and they started me hoping that we still had a chance to make it to *British Venturer* after all.

The trucks roared into life as we clambered hurriedly aboard. We left the elderly German with the Nazi armband staring at the burning wreck with a strange, almost pathetic look of surprised pride. I really hoped he got something good out of it – I knew that the next *Panzerwagen* which came along would most probably kill him.

It still seemed remarkably quiet and deserted. For a city

that was tearing itself to pieces.

We didn't see the road block until we were almost on it.

I'd stayed squatting on those terrifying man-packs of explosive, just hanging on grimly and wishing alternately that I didn't feel quite so utterly useless and that I hadn't lost my cigarettes somewhere in the gutter beside that blazing armoured car back there. Above me, crouched over the top of the cab, my Commando Corporal with the big boots swung the muzzle of his GPMG to cover the road ahead while, all around, British and German kneeling figures swayed and jolted to the motion of the vehicle.

Another explosion to the east, only the flash of it decipherable above the roar of the engine. I glanced round sharply to see the *Hauptmann* looking up too. He caught my eye and his teeth glinted momentarily in the street lights. 'We fight like true Aryans, *ja*? With fire in our bellies and steel in our hands!'

I muttered 'Yeah,' without a lot of excess enthusiasm. He looked at me a little curiously. 'You seem to have very little faith in the success of your NATO landings, *Herr Kapitän* Cable.'

I blinked back nervously. Oh *hell*, but I'd even forgotten the reason that they were making up the numbers of this truckload of homicidal maniacs was because they still thought Cable's Commando was the advance party of a multi-nation seaborne landing, due to take place at . . .

'Zero five hundred hours, *Kapitän*.'

'Eh?'

'Your amphibious forces – they will be assaulting the beaches east and west of here at five o'clock, will they not? In precisely . . .' He peered at his watch in the gloom, '. . . precisely three hours and twenty-two minutes.'

I did a rapid calculation in my head. If we could make it to the docks within, say, another forty-five minutes, it still left us with over two and a half hours to hijack *British Venturer*, turn over her engines and cast off according to schedule. And we'd had a firm intelligence report that she was only guarded by a nominal detachment of Soviet Military Police ... Though I *still* thought we needed two and a half days instead, and even then only if she was guarded by an eighty-five-year-old, pacifist shipkeeper...

But if we didn't make the timetable, and *Herr Hauptmann* Kleiber's thirty thousand violent little Nazi oppo's twigged they were fighting a very lonely, losing war ... I shuddered involuntarily and muttered, 'Zero five hundred on the button, just like you say, *Hauptmann.* Your pathfinder crowd should meet up with them then.'

He smiled again, deprecatingly. 'You disappoint me, *Kapitän.* Not to yet appreciate our resources. Already we have sent a fishing craft with a ... a *Lotse* aboard. A navigating pilot? To offer his services when approaching the coastal waters.'

I stared incredulously, trying desperately to absorb the impact of this latest bombshell. 'You've done *what*, man?'

He looked pleased as Punch when Judy got the chop. 'A *Wiedereinstellung* inshore guide, *Kapitän* Cable. To advise your landing group commanders ... Our people should be meeting the advance elements of your Task Force at any time now. It will be an historic moment for Germany, *ja?*'

I felt the world spin round and round while the nervous tic dragged the corner of my mouth into a savage grimace. They'd have a radio aboard that floating Nazi welcome mat, which meant that – when they'd got tired of sculling around the Baltic in search of a non-existent Allied Task Force that was still in World War Two mothballs – they'd be transmitting a perplexed signal which would upset the Teutonic brass more than a little back at *Führer* Geber's *Armee-Oberkommando* ... and the only Allies currently available for questioning by his volunteer *Gestapo* were ourselves.

Oh *Christ!*

Kleiber's voice sounded suddenly rough and suspicious. '*Was ist los, Herr Kapitän?* You seem very disturbed ...'

Then we hit a fast curve at about fifty miles an hour and,

without warning, I felt the truck's brakes slamming on while we drifted crazily broadside with the tyres screeching in torment and the acrid stench of frictionized rubber in our nostrils. And, temporarily, Kleiber forgot all about my involuntary indiscretion as he clawed his way above the level of the cab, took one look ahead, and started screaming urgently, '*Nicht feuern!* Hold your fire!'

As soon as we'd rocked to a halt I stuck my head cautiously above the side of the lorry, too. And found myself staring into the yawning, chrome framed cavity of a bus window without a splinter of glass left in it.

Then someone in the bus itself stuck the barrel of a Schmeisser machine-pistol into the soft cavity under my left cheek bone. And a very controlled but menacing German voice suggested I should '*Hande hoch . . . Hande hoch, sogleich!*'

I froze there, with my hands towards the night sky, for maybe two hours. Or two minutes? Then slowly, ever so bloody slowly, the cold muzzle of the gun withdrew from my face and I closed my eyes for a long, delicious moment. It was a bit like banging your head against a concrete block – it was such a goddamn relief to stop.

Behind me someone said flatly, 'You can put your hands down now, you heroic bastard!' and I turned to see McReadie grinning sardonically down at me. I lowered my arms slowly and experimentally and, when nobody seemed to resent it, stood up stiffly.

McReadie waved an arm at the barricade of Ahldenstadt Corporation transport drawn across the road. 'It seems that, behind the junk, is Town Hall Square – they call it the *Rathausplatze*. Geber's mob have established one of their main grouping areas here . . . sort of a Brigade HQ and logistics depot in one. We wait a while now until our self-styled *Hauptmann* visits to check on the Soviet units' deployment before we move on to the docks.'

'McReadie.' I whispered urgently, 'They know. Or they damned soon will do . . . about the NATO Task Force.'

He lit two cigarettes and passed one to me absently. 'What NATO Task Force?'

'That, McReadie . . .' I said acidly, '. . . is precisely what I bloody well mean . . .'

He listened impassively as I told him about the utility *Lotse* boat ploughing, this very moment, around an empty Baltic in search of our phantom battle fleet. Then I told him exactly what I thought about BMSNC's capacity for planning bigger and better and more ambitious ways for Brevet Cable to commit suicide on their behalf. And what I personally suggested he and J.C. should do with the good ship *British Venturer*, then – when I'd exhausted my anatomical imagination – I finished heavily with, '. . . so just what, precisely, does your Dartmouth training tell you we should do now, Commander? For when the Geber mob find out they're up a Russian creek without anyone else's Commando carriers?'

He didn't say anything for a long time. He just stood there with the cigarette burning away unnoticed, and gazing at a point somewhere over my shoulder. Then I saw his eyes for the first time. They were the colour of salt water ice. Slowly I pivoted, the hair on my scalp starting to crawl with unimaginable things.

McReadie murmured thoughtfully, 'I think we'll have to be careful, Brev . . . I think we'll have to be very careful indeed.'

I closed my eyes with the shock of it, then forced them open again. Somehow.

The dangling corpses, maybe fifty, sixty of them – it didn't really matter – hung in immaculate down-the-line formation. Swaying gently, twisting clockwise then back again in an obscene, unbelievable pirouette of death, with delicately pointed toes dipping towards the shiny wet gutter immediately below the tautly stretched wires strung from lamp-post to lamp-post.

And only the ungainly set of the shaven heads to spoil the perfection of that monstrous ballet. The tortured, lolling

133

skulls with blue, inhuman faces and black protruding tongues.

And the placards. The white, rough cut squares which formed a pendant around every cadaver's broken neck. With each dead man's label bearing the same charcoal scrawled legend . . . 'KOMMUNIST!'

From a long way away someone whispered, 'Oh God!' in a tone of unutterably sad futility, and I turned to see Chief Reid and Twist, and Ordnance Major Gray and young De'Ath silently watching too. Then the Second Mate swung desperately and we heard him vomiting, but we didn't mind at all, and we didn't think any the less of him for it.

While McReadie murmured flatly, 'In fact, I rather hope they do find out about us now. I really, honestly hope to God they do . . .'

The first Soviet tank hit the *Rathausplatze* five minutes later.

Actually, even before that – when Kleiber first rejoined us – he wasn't looking quite as enthusiastic about the rebirth of the Fourth Reich as he had done. In fact *Hauptmann* Kleiber seemed to be a very disillusioned man, but I still thought viciously that he'd have looked even sicker if he'd realized that, from now on, every member of his lorry-borne *Aufklarungsabteilung* was being surreptitiously covered by a Royal Marine sub-machine-gun muzzle. And that the paternal way our Colour Sergeant Lattice stayed behind him was given a faintly hypocrytical colouring because of the ten-inch commando stiletto concealed up the Colour Sergeant's sleeve.

Kleiber reached us just as the first really close bursts of firing shattered the silence from the other side of the square. Then there was a dull, slamming noise followed by a brilliant flash which immediately died to a duller red glow above the far roofs, and we watched the oily black column of smoke – dappled orange touching its undersides – as it climbed into the sky.

Kleiber glanced back nervously and his features seemed white and drawn. He said, 'We go now! We must hurr . . .'

Then another gigantic door slammed, and the oily cloud got bigger, while De'Ath snarled, '*Quiet*, there!' And we watched, and listened with straining ears to that secondary sound – the far-off, unnerving rumble and squeak of the most terrifying early warning I'd ever experienced.

Lattice said, matter of factly, 'Tanks, sir. Loadin' phosphorous rounds, God 'elp that lot out there.'

I threw a glance of revulsion at the silent, still revolving rank of cadavers, and thought He probably wouldn't bother. Not after that. Then Kleiber called more urgently, 'We go now, *Kapitän*! Before *der Sowjet ankommen.*'

Which I thought personally was a bloody good idea too.

Except that McReadie had to go and say, with immeasurable and unhurried satisfaction, 'They're kicking you right up the arse already, aren't they, *Herr Hauptmann*? Right up every lily-white, pure-Aryan bottom with a Swastika stamped across it?'

I saw the suddenly wary look in Kleiber's eyes as he tried to understand what was happening to his Allies' goodwill. I also saw the way his finger slipped carefully into the trigger guard of that bloody Schmeisser of his. Curiously everything seemed to get very quiet, but it could only have been in my mind because all hell was starting to break loose across the square, less than two hundred yards from us.

McReadie's foresight lifted ever so slightly. 'You met up with our Task Force yet, *Hauptmann* . . .? Or have your boys in black been too busy building up a hanging tally for the new look *Gestatspolizei*? Because, Kleiber, those NATO assault ships just aren't go . . .'

Then I noticed Lattice moving in closer behind Kleiber, and the expression on Kleiber's face as he stared from McReadie to the hanging men and suddenly understood McReadie's hatred. But I also remembered a ship – a very deadly ship which could kill more people in a millisecond's flash than a host of dedicated monsters like Kleiber and

Geber had managed to do in six years of factory-planned genocide – so I shouted, 'Shut up, McReadie . . .!'

And, not even knowing fully what I was doing but only knowing that I would, I brought my own AK round to slam into McReadie's belly at the same moment that I threw the safety selector to 'Automatic'. And, with the sweat rolling down my face, whispered, '. . . or, by Christ, I'll blow your guts out, Commander . . . I'll take away your spine before I let your delayed bloody conscience smash up this operation now, so help me God but I will!'

He gazed into my eyes for a long time, maybe looking for something that wasn't there, and ever so slowly I observed the old McReadie grin smooth away the hate. Then gently, carefully, he pushed the muzzle of my gun away.

And said, 'Thanks . . . Mate!' And I knew he really meant it.

But I was still glad he'd done what he did – McReadie, I mean. Because I knew now that he had feelings sometimes, too.

De'Ath shouted urgently, 'Mount up!' and we scrambled back into the trucks at the precise moment that the first phosphorous shell slammed into the square itself. I half turned as I hauled myself over the tailboard to see a long, expanding tentacle of pure white heat leaping and bounding across the rain-swept plateau, then the tentacle reached out just a little further and engulfed a lorry with a red, white and black Nazi flag fluttering gaily above a platform crammed with men.

Until there was only roaring flame with just a *soupçon* of screaming and, all the time, the rumbling squeal of the tank tracks echoing in the middle distance as they came nearer. And nearer.

And then the nightmare of it all became very personal indeed when a little baby flame broke mischievously from its rampaging mother and ran on melting, demented legs towards us. Everybody, British and German alike, stood in appalled horror as the vagrant fire with the beating arms

136

and the monstrous, bubbling head stumbled blindly closer with tiny bits of blazing, smoking somethings leaving a twinkling trail which just wouldn't be extinguished even then.

I was only dimly aware of Kleiber's Schmeisser rising before it hammered racketingly alongside me, and the runaway furnace stopped running and went over backwards in a jerking, gratefully-disintegrating smear of phosphorescence, then – an eternity later – the Schmeisser stopped yammering abruptly as the bolt slammed forward on an empty magazine, while the *Hauptmann*'s features wore an expression of such infinite compassion that I knew then I would never understand. And turned my back on the insoluble anomaly of the hideously hanging men and the mercifully ended recipient of Kleiber's nine-millimetre euthanasia.

The last image we retained of the burning *Rathausplatze* was of a lot of little black, running figures pouring from a side street, desperately fanning out over the square itself. And every single figure knelt doggedly to fire back at the huge hull of the Soviet T54 tank which was shepherding them ahead of it. Until the front of the tank rippled with tiny darts of flame and the black figures started to go down under the vectoring tracer streams . . .

I felt the ghost rejoin me, then. That one-legged, dead old sea captain called Viktorovich Mikhail Pritytsky. And he stayed right behind my hunched shoulder all the way down that long, nerve-racking road towards the docks.

And towards *British Venturer*.

Kleiber went in the second truck for the last lap. I don't really think he was so much scared as that he'd had the guts knocked out of him to find that his Nazi Phoenix was being shoved right back into the Soviet fire just as soon as it stuck its rapacious head above the grate. I also reflected bitterly that Admiral Sir James Cromer, VC etc., must be feeling very, very pleased with himself right now, with the mutilated remains of the *Wiedereinstellung* dying even quicker than he could ever have hoped for . . .

It still made me a bit more optimistic, though. Maybe, if he'd been right about that, then he'd also be right about the next assumption – that the dock area should now be virtually deserted by Russian and East German Army units in order to cope with the existing pressure on their flanks. And not even my resigned brain could visualize the Ahldenstadt Area Military Commandant leaving much of a watch-keeping force around here while he risked the remaining Nazis digging in and consolidating to the east.

Not when he was bound to assume that it was only a local resistance gesture anyway – and he had a line of coastal radar stations from here to the Gulf of Gdansk to assure him that the phantom NATO Task Force was really only a wistful twinkle in *Führer* Geber's eye. In fact I would lay odds it was going to take the truncheon wielding MVD and *Vopos* interrogators a lot of good professional toil and sweat before they even half-started to believe why several thousand Nazi plotters had suddenly upped and, apparently, committed suicide with great enthusiasm. But that, for a blessed change, wasn't Cable's problem.

Anyway, I had enough worries of my own right now. Like stealing a ship before Kleiber twigged he'd been had. We might still be needing all the help we could get between here and *Venturer*, even though I'd virtually convinced myself we were practically home and dry without a Russian soldier posted this side of the *Rathausplatze*.

But of course Kleiber's driver just had to go and spoil it all again.

By bringing us to a screeching, juddering halt virtually gun muzzle to gun muzzle with precisely one of those same Russian military units that couldn't possibly have been here in the first bloody place. Not according to Cable's strategic analysis, anyway.

Though the *real* snag about it was that, while we had a gun muzzle which sported a bore of considerably less than one inch, the opposition packed a 100-millimetre-wide orifice at the end of the three-mile-long barrel sticking out of the turret of their Soviet T54 tank.

And *I* scrambled to my feet just in time to find myself actually looking straight *down* it, f'r Chrissakes . . .

I found out later – when I could actually speak again – that, while I'd been speculating on the wider aspects of the conflict, the rest of the OPERATION STAYSAIL team had been concentrating on the more practical problem of making it to *Venturer* without getting our tails shot off in the process . . . and none of us seemed to be much damned good at what we'd been doing.

Because we'd broadsided round a right-angle bend in the deserted road in such a hurry that our driver just didn't have room to take avoiding action when he saw thirty tons of T54 squatting stolidly as a marble dam across his course. He'd done everything but scrape his boot soles along the road to stop us but it had still meant that – while the second truck had managed to shave through a gap minus its paint – we, including me, had force-parked immaculately on the angry end of the monster.

It was the second time that night that someone had poked a gun at my head as I stuck it over the back of the cab. Except that this one made the Nazi Schmeisser seem like a pipe stem to a railway tunnel. The other difference was that, this time, I didn't freeze at all. I just took one incredulous, utterly terrified glance into the high explosive maw that was about to decapitate me with a hundred thousand foot pound smack in the eye, then hurled myself backwards with the unreasoning reflex of sheer, gibbering terror.

I suppose, on reflection, that the Soviet tank crew were just as surprised as we were – though maybe not quite so shattered. I remember lying flat on my back across the suddenly preferable man-packs of TNT, and staring up at an equally dazed tank commander as he stood clutching earphones to his chest and with shoulders half-out of his turret.

Then my Marine Corporal nervously squeezed the trigger of his heavy machine-gun and the tank commander's chest disappeared in a red haze of shining spray while the rest of him tumbled sloppily back below turret level.

Someone from the stern of the lorry started screaming, '*Ruckseite! Ruckseite!*' which probably meant 'Let's get the hell outa here backwards!' in German. Then I found out with incredible impact that I wasn't the only one around who acted on nervous impulse.

As the Soviet gunlayer convulsively fired a 100 millimeter HE round within three feet of my ear.

During that demoralized eternity I'd just gaped at the milled steel ring forming the end of the gun barrel, and noted vaguely that it was immaculately clean with just the faintest patina of oil highlighting the Russian characters stamped into it. Then the Corporal's machine-gun stopped racketing abruptly as he found there wasn't anything but four-inch-thick armour-plated *Panzer* left to fire at.

And then the huge muzzle flash of the tank gun had cloven the night while the shock wave blasted us around the platform of the truck like dandelion puffs in a force twelve gale, and the reeking gases of the expanded cordite turned our mouths to gaping, idiot holes sucking in the poisoned air.

I was dimly conscious of an unbearable pain in my pressurized skull, and that Kleiber's Nazis who'd been at the after end of the lorry – ahead of the muzzle and in the main force of the blast – were clutching shattered eardrums in threshing agony, before I found myself blinking dazedly at the skipping, sparking flight of the shell as it supersonicked down the length of the dark street until, ricocheting crazily, it finally exploded in a distant flash of fire.

Suddenly – out of bedlam – a hand gripped my shoulder and literally dragged me away from under the still smoke-spewing muzzle. An image of a white-faced, slightly shocked Colour Sergeant Lattice bellowing noiseless obscenities into my deafened, over-killed ear, then I was rolling over and over under the force of his thrust while the firing pin came out of the grenade he held in his hand.

And the same hand did a sort of conjuring trick before the end of the beautifully oiled barrel and, disconcertingly, came away with nothing held in it at all.

Then Lattice and the Corporal were banging even more urgently on the lorry cab until, vaguely penetrating my singing brain, the crash and screech of engaging gears as we roared backwards, away from the armoured, shiny breast with the red star . . . Seven. Six. Five . . .

Footbrake on. *Slam*. Thassit, now full ahea . . .

A catapulting mêlée of rolling bodies and flailing limbs as we surged back to the tailboard. 'Declutch! De*clutch* you lazy, idle, pure-Aryan bast . . .

Three. TWO . . .! The abused engine revving in sheer terror, then the tailboard slamming forward and we were roaring, skidding around the bulk of the T54 with the crumpled shards of our amputated wings and passenger door compacting frenziedly into the track assembly alongside.

Until we were finally clear and racing for the red tail lights of McReadie's truck while the last milliseconds of grenade fuse sputtered its life away against the nose cone of an automatically reloaded 100 millimetre high explosive tank shell, fused for impact and sitting snugly in its polished, spiralled breech housing.

. . . One second.

Zeroooooooooo!

The four-ton turret section of the T54 lifted clear of its traverse ring with all the exquisite grace of a slow motion ballet sequence . . . a Russian ballet. Curiously, it seemed to hang in mid-air for a very long time, with its underside all shimmering and flickering from the reflected colour of the lights sparkling on and off within the hull. Then a great, roaring ball of phosphorescence erupted from the cavity, and reached up and devoured the hanging turret. And the hull itself blew up with monstrous force as the turret dropped back into the holocaust. And the gable ends of the houses on either side couldn't stand it any longer so they too collapsed into the sea of white-hot, molten metal . . .

. . while Lattice glanced, a bit chuffed, at the shattered Corporal. And the Corporal stared at the fires of hell astern and hollered, 'Holy Mary Anna! I mean, f'r . . . Oh, Holy fuggin' Mar . . .!'

Until Colour Sergeant Lattice snapped irritably, 'Look to your front, Corporal! Jus' like a *proper* bloody Marine . . .'

Then winked at me.

We pulled up beside the ship a few minutes later. There didn't seem to be anybody around at all.

Yet that – curiously enough – seemed to be the most unnerving thing which had happened to me all night.

Seven

The gangway was illuminated by a cluster of cargo lamps, yellow cones of brilliance cutting warm patterns against the slab-sided blackness of *British Venturer*'s hull and, even despite my nervousness, I couldn't help looking up at her with the critical eye of a professional seaman, noting the slightly-too-slack springs and headropes, with the discs of the rat guards secured just a little more askew than I would have tolerated as her master.

She was lying just as I'd left her, starboard side to, and, as I gazed up at her high boat-deck, there was something niggling at the back of my mind about her. Something not quite right in the tidy geometry of white-painted boats and fore and aft trimmed ventilators. Then I suddenly realized what it was – I was looking up at the side on which First Mate Ritchie and young Timson had died, but there wasn't any sign of the ravages caused by the Soviet destroyer's fire, and of the shattered boats and colandered bulkheads I'd remembered from the last time I'd looked along that morgue of a deck.

They'd repaired and repainted her, even to the extent of fitting new boats and davits. God only knew why, unless it was to eradicate all evidence of Red over-zealousness. Ironically it didn't matter under the circumstances anyway – no one would be taking photographs where she was going to be lying in a few hours from now.

But first we had to run the gauntlet of that quiet, apparently deserted stretch of wharf, then climb the accommodation ladder under the glare of those damned arc lamps. While all it needed was one man aboard *Venturer*, one man with a sub machine-gun and an element of calculated cunning, to convert the barren plain of Berth E North, Port of Ahldenstadt, to a bloody killing ground.

Lieutenant De'Ath whispered quietly, 'Carry on, Colour Sergeant.'

I hugged the tailboard of the lorry a little bit closer and glanced along the row of black-streaked faces. They were all gazing up at the ship – McReadie, Twist, Reid, Gray – all with the same look of resolute apprehension. Oddly enough Kleiber seemed calmer now, more settled than he'd been after his series of traumatic shocks back at the *Rathausplatze*. But then – the *Rathausplatze* had been a pretty shocking place in a lot of ways . . . Glancing at the *Hauptmann* curiously I wondered how he felt, knowing we were shortly to be sailing out into the free blue yonder and leaving him to face the Russian music which was now – according to the distant sounds of battle – working rapidly up to a base crescendo of almost pure hundred millimetre gunfire.

Then, just as I was steeling myself for the Death or Glory charge, Colour Sergeant Lattice nodded briefly to the big Marine Corporal who'd spent most of the night treading on my hands, whereupon the Corporal stepped casually forward into the centre of the pool of light from the ship. And whistled cockily – just like Jiminy Cricket!

I stared incredulously. Where was the superbly suave, surreptitious killer's approach? The mythical commando figure gliding stealthily and unseen, an imperceptible ripple of menace in the night? They were supposed to be *silent* assassins, these Marines – not chirruping bloody idiots who blundered naïvely across the opposition's front doorstep like a floodlit invitation to a shoot.

The Corporal whistled again. Dammit, he wasn't even trying to rush the ladder. He just stood there instead, hands in pockets, gun cradled under arm like a ploughboy on a rabbit walk and head interestedly craned backwards to inspect the huge bulk of *Venturer* above him.

I started to sweat, despite the chill in my bones.

Along from me a Marine eased the barrel of his automatic

rifle to line up with *Venturer*'s silent deck. I thought bitterly, 'F'r cryin' out loud, but if they intend to start *shooting* it'll home every Red unit within . . .' Then De'Ath's voice whispered sharply, 'As you were,' and I knuckled my forehead in bewildered disgust.

The big Corporal whistled a little louder. It grew very still, out there in the rain with the drips from the shiny wet roofs of the warehouses pattering relentlessly on the backs of our crouching, waiting figures. No one moved an inch . . .

. . . or did they?

Up there on the centrecastle-deck? Beside the forward accommodation entrance? The glint of reflected light on metal . . . on a *gun* barrel . . . then the Corporal shouted petulantly, 'Anyone at 'ome up there?' so I just closed my eyes and gave up worrying altogether.

Until a dim figure stepped forward from the shadows of the ship, and raised the barrel of his Soviet Decteriov at precisely the same moment as I heard a funny, twanging slam from beside me. Whereupon the guard aboard *Venturer* stopped being curious and, instead, performed an unexpectedly convulsive pirouette while, at the same time, plucking ineffectually at the steel rod which had skewered his neck.

Immediately De'Ath snapped, without any surprise at all, 'Go . . . *One!*'

Upon which the Corporal stopped playing silly buggers and took the accommodation ladder steps three at a time, followed by the first of the crouching Marines. They hit the deck at the top already on their way down to the prone position, and suddenly we had two men aboard *Venturer* with automatic weapons covering fore and aft.

De'Ath's controlled command again. 'Go, Two! Go . . . Three!'

Until a chain of running, shadowy shapes cut across that exposed wharf and we had at least established a foothold aboard the ship itself. It still worried me, though. The fact that no one else had fired at us. There should have been more guards than that one poor devil who'd clawed so frantical . . . I swung round towards the man beside me, curiously looking to see how you can kill a human being from a long way away, and not even let anyone else know you were doing so.

The steel crossbow was quite a technological improvement on the original English archer's model used at Agincourt. But the face above it was the same as the British soldier's had been for hundreds of years and – quite illogically – that's what made me feel so confident when I was with Marine Colour Sergeant Lattice . . . he was such a thoroughly *nice* man.

When he was on your side.

It felt good and, somehow, more comforting – being aboard a ship again. But the feeling didn't last long. I mean, no seaman could be at ease when he knows he soon has to sink his command with the cold impersonality of a public hangman.

Actually, there were two additional factors which added to my unease. The first was the way Kleiber still stayed staring up at the ship, almost like a lost little boy. I'd hesitated before I left him and our eyes had met and held for a long time, then I'd allowed mine to drop guiltily because I knew he would be dead in a short time from now while he still thought he was doing something pretty patriotic and brave, in his distorted, blind sort of allegiance.

Or did he . . .? Maybe the way he'd accepted our going was what made me feel so nervous. The way he'd stuck out his hand and those strong white teeth had flashed briefly against the sweat mask of shiny black. '*Auf Wiedersehen, Herr Kapitän*,' he'd said. And I'd looked along the exhausted, shocked faces of his surviving men, most of them still suffering from the blast of that tank round, and felt like the biggest bastard since their own Adolph Hitler about the way we were sacrificing them.

But it wasn't until I was actually aboard *Venturer* that I

realized what had been missing down there – that *Hauptmann* Kleiber had omitted the one thing which no utterly convinced second generation Nazi would have overlooked on this night of all nights . . . That he hadn't thrown me the inevitable, straight-arm salute as I'd turned away. So could that really mean that he'd actually *guessed* what was happening – maybe after McReadie's taunting – and lost his patriotic zeal?

Yet, if he had, then why in God's name did he accept it so passively?

And the second factor which made me stay all cold and sick inside was the dead sentry – the twisted, incongruously lone guardian who still huddled like a small child against the stark white bulkhead. He certainly didn't look like a Russian, but then again, he didn't look all that much like a German or a Swede or a Liverpool Irishman either. Not with a bloodstained, eighteen inch steel skewer protruding from his throat. But the most oddly disturbing thing about him was the way he was dressed.

Because surely neither Soviet, nor East German Army nor *Vopos* guards, would normally wear stained jeans and a cable-stitched pullover while they were on duty?

I didn't have time to worry right then, though. We had a ship to hijack and a booby-trapped thermo-nuclear bomb to defuse.

It was still curious, all the same . . . about the inexplicably phlegmatic Kleiber and the corpse with the woolly jumper.

It was about then that things first started to go wrong.

Lieutenant De'Ath met me at the engine-room access door. 'My men have taken a quick shufti round the decks, sir. But we can't be sure there's no one else aboard unless you want us to check out the accommodation.'

I shook my head tiredly, not really knowing what to do but aware that, whatever I decided, I could still be very wrong. 'No, leave the search till we're out at sea, Lieutenant. The last thing we want just now is to spark off a shooting war that'll let everyone within five miles know we're here.'

He looked dubious. 'I don't like it. It just doesn't add up . . . For instance, where's the guard, sir? Apart from that chap at the gangway the whole damned ship's like a morgue . . .'

I cut in savagely, 'You coin an unfortunate phrase, don't you, Lieutenant . . .? No. Let sleeping dogs lie as quiet as we can until we can afford a noise – apart from the fact that it would tie up your men for hours, searching every corner of a ship this size.'

He nodded stiffly. I could see I'd hurt him and it made me think back a million years to when a certain Chief Officer had caught me on the raw. I'd lashed out at him too, in nervous anger. Just before he took a walk along a boat-deck that had exploded under him.

Awkwardly I muttered, 'Sorry, Lieutenant. It's just that . . . Ah, the hell with it. But I'm damned glad you're here.'

The youngster smiled softly into the glow from the engine-room. 'It's a funny thing, sir . . .' he murmured sincerely. '. . . But so am I. Terribly glad indeed.'

Chief Reid was firmly in command of the engine-room control platform by the time I'd slid down the long, shiny, ladder handrails and inhaled great, nostalgic whiffs of the smell of ship – of hot oil and tar, and paint and asbestos lagging. He glanced up from the row of dials as I arrived and I searched his impassive features anxiously for any indication of unexpected snags.

He said briefly, 'I can have her ready for sea in about twenty minutes . . . if you're no' too worried about a proper run-up on the main engines.'

I forced a grin. 'I don't give a monkey's if you have to turn 'em by handles, Chief. Just so long as you can get us out've here without any problems.'

He didn't smile back and I felt the grin fading to make way for that familiar nervous tic. There *was* something wrong, then? But what, for God's sake? He'd already said he could

148

move her pretty soon, and I could hear number two starboard generator already humming away down there below the platform, so we didn't have electric power troubles . . .

I asked sharply, 'What's up, Chief? What's wrong with her?'

Reid threw the switch in the main feedline to the master gyro. 'Nothing, Captain! Nothing mechanical, anyroad . . . But maybe ye'd better hae a word wi' Commander McReadie? He's down at number four deep tank bulkhead with Major Gray. Down there at yon bloody bomb of theirs.'

The bomb! I closed my eyes for a moment of pure terror, then opened them again guiltily, ashamed at having displayed my fears so openly before Reid. He pretended not to notice, though. He just threw another switch and said quickly, 'Och, it's no' the bomb that's a problem . . . not yet, anyway.'

Half-way down the next flight of ladders I heard his voice again over the whine of the jenny. '. . . and anyhow, if it does become one, Captain, I'm thinking we'll be the very first people in the world to find it out.'

I went on down to the bottom of the ship. I'd never realized before how lonely the engine space could be, and how utterly terrifying – when you're expecting someone to shoot you quite dispassionately every time you turn a corner.

Especially if your only intangible companion is a one-legged, Soviet spectre. And a not particularly friendly one at that.

McReadie wasn't exactly one helluva lot enthusiastic about my company either, when I finally arrived. I found both him and Gray bending over the plate bolted to the bulkhead and thought wryly that you'd never have guessed what lay behind it, not judging by the way Gray was wielding that ring spanner like a mechanic on piece work. But then, we didn't have a lot of time for finesse. Not until it came to the actual disarming process, anyway – please God.

The Commander barely glanced up at me and the ex-

149

pression on his features matched the frustrated one I'd just left on the Chief's. I ignored the enthusiastic welcome and asked urgently, 'For Chrissakes, but will someone tell me why everyone down here's gone so bloody peculiar?'

The Major hesitated in the act of removing another nut and, just for a moment, he and McReadie glanced at each other. Then McReadie gestured abruptly towards the dark recess behind the silent, unused port generator casing, and said bitterly, '*That's* what's the matter, Cable . . . If you haven't got anything else to do right now.'

I retorted nastily, 'I already sent Twist up to the bridge to check out the steering gear and telegraphs, and just happened to think the Major there might need an expert hand . . . except I see he's already *got* a bloody atomic scientist's labourer in you, Comman . . .'

Then I saw what lay behind the casing of the jenny and, after slamming backwards with the shock of it, averted my eyes and stared fixedly at nothing.

'Take another look, Cable.' McReadie grated from behind me, 'Take a proper look an' tell me if you don't think there's something a bit odd about this stinking death ship too.'

I was aware of the sweat trickling into my eyes and dragged my hand savagely across them to clear it. Then – because I knew that there was something terribly wrong – I took a mental grip on my heaving stomach and forced myself to go back round and look at the mutilated thing that had once been a man.

'Congratulations, McReadie,' I heard myself saying tightly, 'And did you empty a whole magazine into his belly before or after you tipped the poor sod over the rail from sixty feet up?'

The only good thing about it was that I now knew what had happened to at least part of the guard. And this one had even been properly dressed – I could still see the blood-stained Russian service cap protruding from under the otherwise unidentifiable and impacted cadaver. That made me feel a bit easier, apart from the nausea.

Until McReadie said slowly, 'But that's the most curious thing about it, Cable . . . Because none of us here *did* kill him. We just found it lying here when we came below . . .

'. . . It means that the original guard was massacred before we even came aboard, Cable. It means that someone else – and certainly not the Reds – has more than a passing interest in *British Venturer*.'

De'Ath had apparently gone when I got to deck level again. I stepped over the low coaming from the engine-room entrance and, just for a few moments, leaned shakily against the cold steel plating while my battered mind shrieked a nebulous warning of things unspecified – of things yet to happen against which the previous horrors of the night would fade into obscurity.

I levered myself upright, gripping the polished stock of my AK with the desperate dependence of a very frightened man. Forward, framed in the rectangle of the dimly lit alleyway, I could see the humped outlines of winches and derricks and ventilators. And every black shape could conceal a pair of eyes – alien eyes. Already sighting along the barrel of the gun that was going to kill me . . . Killer's eyes. Implacable, hate-filled eyes . . .

I blinked. Talking about eyes – where were *ours*, f'r crying out loud? Where were the British eyes? The sentries who should be guarding the top of the accommodation ladder . . . ? I stumbled cautiously to the rail and looked over, down on to the wet, silent wharf, but nothing moved under the skeletal shadows of the high cranes. Even Kleiber had gone, and the grey-faced, shuffling *Wiedereinstellung* survivors. Back to await the oblivion offered by a Soviet bullet or a phosphorous blanket, or a blackjack . . .

. . . but it still didn't explain why our Commando wasn't around any more.

I started moving blindly towards the bridge. Twist was up there, along with Colour Sergeant Lattice and two Marines. Maybe he'd understand what was happening.

Because maybe his young, resilient mind wouldn't be as full of ghosts and bloody silly horror-film images as mine was.

The boat-deck looked just the same as it had done the moment before a Russian destroyer captain had said 'Fire!' Except maybe the paint was a little fresher and the planking a little newer . . . then, suddenly, I couldn't stop running, not with the terror in me like it was. All I knew was that I had to get up that ladder to the bridge, to see Twist and Lattice and as many resolute British faces as I could.

I hit the bottom of the ladder with the muscles in my back knotted into great kinks of fine-spun wire, almost feeling the smash of machine-gun bullets stitching across my kidneys. Just in time I remembered our own nervous reflexes might be equally fallible, and that the shells might just come from my front instead, so I gabbled, 'It's Cable! Hold your fire 'cause I'm *Cable* . . .'

Until I hauled myself over the top step and found that nobody intended to shoot me after all.

Because there just wasn't anybody there to pull a trigger.

For a long time I stood there out on the wing of the bridge, feeling the rain pattering with ridiculous normality on my cold, trembling face and trying desperately to understand. Then I took a grip on my bewildered senses and, with the AK thrust jumpily before me, forced myself through the open wheelhouse door and into the dark, secret space within.

But there was still nothing. Not a movement, not a sound. Only the dull brass gleam of long unpolished tele-graphs and barometer and binnacle cover. I heard myself draw a great, shuddering breath of incredulity – it seemed that I was, quite suddenly, the only man left aboard *British Venturer* because this *was* the bridge, and there should be a lot of men up here preparing to steal a ship. Either up here or down below with McReadie and the Chief . . .

Grabbing the telephone from its receiver I stabbed the call button desperately. God but I had to hear someone else talking – to prove that I was wrong and that this crazy, macabre isolation was only a quirk of coincidence – that maybe Twist and his crowd had gone down the port side ladder just as I'd come up the starb . . .

A tinny, distant voice said suspiciously into my ear, 'Engine-room. Who's that speakin'?'

I felt the waves of relief swamping over me in an almost pure adrenalin tide. Forcing myself to speak casually I said, 'Cable, Chief. Is . . . ah . . . is Mister Twist down there with you?'

There was a brief hesitation – nothing I could pin down, but a fractional delay nevertheless – then he answered stiffly, 'No. There's nobody here but me.'

I frowned into the receiver. What the *hell* was getting into Chief Reid? And why the reticence? I snapped more sharply, 'So what about the Commander and the Major? Aren't they still down there too?'

Again the coy delay. Until, 'Aye . . . Aye, they'll be down here still. At the deep tank bulkhead.'

Irritably sarcastic I said heavily, 'Thank you very *much* for being such a bloody mine of informa . . .'

Then I stopped speaking, and just stood there frozen, with the telephone in my hand and the rain beating against the wheelhouse windows in softly sighing spasms. While the cargo lamps on the foremast started to swing under the touch of the freshening wind and to throw yellow orbs of light in ever-widening circles across the bridge . . . and each spiral of the light briefly illuminated the man who sat out there in the corner of the port wing, just staring fixedly and penetratingly.

Right *at* me.

I felt the screaming sweat of near hysteria bathing my face as, without taking my eyes off the other man for an instant, I numbly replaced the telephone on its hook without even waiting for a reply from the recalcitrant Chief Engineer a million miles below my feet. Then slowly, hesitantly, I edged across the wheelhouse and out on to the open area of deck.

And stood looking down. While the man just sat looking

up with wide, surprised eyes which didn't seem to mind the droplets of rain that entered them from the night sky, because he didn't move even fractionally from the slumped, relaxed pose he'd taken up in the corner.

There was something else a bit odd about him too, and that was his face. Oh, not so much the shocked, even slightly aggrieved expression it wore as the colour – the suffused, mottled blue-black shade of death, visible even under the patina of dirt and oil.

It made him look so undignified and untidy, which was a pity. Because he'd been such a very smart soldier, the last time I'd seen him down on the dock.

Marine Colour Sergeant Lattice, I mean.

But that had been before someone else had tried their hand at the Colour Sergeant's trade. And, really, they'd strangled him with a very high degree of expertise at that – except that they'd made the one cardinal mistake in technique which he would have found unforgivable . . .

. . . seeing they'd used a bit o' bloody *cheesewire*, f'r Chrissakes.

Though admittedly with such finesse that they'd still left the Colour Sergeant's head sitting square on the broad, military shoulders. Or at least – *nearly* square on the broad milita . . .

I started to stumble away as though every scaly, reptilian product of a madman's brain was dragging itself aboard this fifty megaton coffin. I didn't care anymore, I just had to get away, anywhere but on that blood-spattered bridge with its self-reproaching, semi-decapitated occupant.

Because it does something to your faith – when you finally realize, with all the attendant horror – that an old, old soldier like the good indestructible Lattice *can* still die dreadfully. And not just fade away.

Like you'd always been promised. In the story books.

McReadie. I just had to get to McReadie . . .

Still nobody around on the lower-decks. I half-fell over

the low coaming, backing into the glare and smell of the engine-room, hands reaching for the oil-smeared handrails leading down, down to McReadie and the Major and – please God – normality. Or could any normality exist in a place where two men are about to defuse a rogue hydrogen bomb . . .? Ah, the *hell* with it! When my Gods were proved only flesh and blood and white, trailing sinew, then my neat orderly little world of make-believe just couldn't cope any longer.

I looked for the Chief on the platform. But *he* wasn't there any more, either.

Oh, *Jesus*!

Stumbling painfully I slid helter-skelter down the first run of ladder to the bed plates. Maybe it was the shock of that slip which seemed to jolt my mind back to its usual state of being just plain, ordinary scared – but at least without that terrible, unreasoning horror of the unknown.

And I did still have my image to think of – that coldly calculating Cable smile with just a hint of raw courage, sneering in the face of evil . . . I steadied myself, patted the stock of the AK grimly, took a hard-eyed, rugged survey round the cavernous maze of pipes and diced steel ladder-work above me – thought I saw a menacing movement from the starboard side of the control platform . . .

. . . and fell down the last flight of steel rungs in yet another surge of sheer undiluted terror. But that's the trouble with being a coward – you get frightened so easily.

Please, God, let McReadie be down here . . . Don't let me find I'm still alone, not again. Not just me down here with only that smashed, bloody corpse of a Russian soldier. And the spectre of a long dead, one-legged master mariner . . .

McReadie's voice said tightly, 'Stay absolutely still, Cable! Right where you are. Or shove off out of it.'

Slowly I turned. Then I saw what the Major was doing, and stopped turning. Along with breathing and pretty near everything else. I even forgot momentarily about the silent, frighteningly empty ship around me and the blankly resentful eyes of my fallen God on that rainswept bridge.

While Ordnance Major Gray took the fused lid off the biggest bloody bomb in the whole world.

McReadie and I watched him gently, ever so gently, unscrew the last retaining nut from the ring of studs before – with only the faintest suspicion of a wry glance at us – the Major eased what was now virtually an independent trigger away from its seating.

Maybe I wouldn't have felt quite so bad if I hadn't known what he was up against. But I did – because he'd already told me all about it when I was elected stand-in bomb disposal specialist in the event of the Major's premature shuffling off this Mortal Coil on the end of a Soviet bullet. And *that* was another of the things which hurt me about BMSNC – They build you up to the fine pitch of being convinced you're indispensable, then you arrive on the job to find some complete technological dimwit like McReadie telling you *he's* assisting in the operation instead, so go sail your bloody boat, Cable . . .

Not that I would have minded. Not this time around. Not when I found that watching someone else risking the mistake that would cremate you, too, was even worse than committing your own personal brand of suicide.

Because there were those five wires, and that micro-switch and the two clip fuses. And they all had to be cut or switched off or withdrawn in precisely the right sequence, otherwise . . .

. . . and then there was what Gray had called the 'Deactivating Tolerance'. The maximum distance that the plate could be removed from the plane of the bulkhead to give access while rendering the firing circuit harmless. That allowable gap of precisely nine point three eight centimetres . . .

Gray murmured conversationally, 'I'm cutting the Alfa Lead . . . *Now*.'

The nervous tic started jumping at the side of my jaw.

The Major's hand slid delicately, probingly, into the critical space. 'Removing the micro-switch cover . . . breaking the primary transmission circuit . . .'

I watched in hypnotic fascination as a droplet of sweat hung shimmering from the underside of his chin. '. . . *Now.*'

McReadie whispered hopefully, 'Is that the lot, then?' and the Major snapped back, 'Just shut up an' hold this, laddie!' which pleased me a great deal in spite of the tension because it was nice to see McReadie being treated like a drivelling idiot instead of me for a change. And *I* knew the Major hadn't finished yet. Not by a long, super-heated way.

McReadie took the weight of the steel cover as delicately as if it was made of eggshell and smoke. He didn't need telling again that, if he allowed it to move further than the breadth of a man's hand, he would only be one of a million billion tiny incandescent sparks in a twenty mile wide bonfire.

Gray flexed his cramped hand and grinned reassuringly up to where I still stood like a piece of the engines. Unmoving. 'Relax, dear boy. I do promise to call you if I make a mistake.'

I tried to think of something classical and terribly debonair to answer back but I found I couldn't speak too good so I just twisted the corner of my mouth weakly and hoped it looked like a ruggedly phlegmatic, specialist-to-specialist acknowledgement.

The Major selected another pair of forceps-like wire cutters from his kit and nodded to McReadie. 'I'll take it again, Commander. Golden rule of the trade, old boy – two hands directed by one brain immeasurably superior to one hand each, but directed by two brains . . . Ready?'

McReadie nodded fractionally. It was the first time in my life I'd ever remembered seeing him quite so introspective. But sitting on a hydrogen bomb is rather apt to have a sobering effect on the layman, just like anything else you don't understand . . . and that made me remember again that there were a lot more things I didn't understand about this crazy night where people disappeared, and indestructible men were destroyed.

Gray took a firm grip on the steel plate with his left hand, but I couldn't watch him any longer so I raised my eyes and my gun to scan the network of ladders and piping above us. So where *was* the Chief, for God's sake? I'd only spoken to him on the phone minutes before my unreasoning dash down here from the bridge. And De'Ath and the men who should have been covering us – because if they *had* been inexplicably spirited away, then shouldn't I be up top instead? Watching and waiting and guarding over the man who was playing with eternity? Or should we even be going ahead with this part of the operation at all?

Then the Major murmured, 'Cutting Echo Victor Red . . .' while I heard the snip of the shears over the steady throb of Two Starboard generator. And I couldn't stop looking at what he was doing a moment longer, so I ignored the threatening engine space above me and just watched as he withdrew the first fuse with all the tenderness of an obstetrician delivering a child.

He half turned, still holding the plate firmly in one hand and the fuse in the other. 'Now, at least, we have a little time . . .' he said with tremendous satisfaction, but I didn't really know what he meant because all he'd told me was the physical sequence of deactivation, and not the results of each individual operation.

Then it all started to go wrong when – with appalling abruptness – his eyes went blank with shock as he glanced up at, and behind my shoulder, to the control platform. And started to scream a warning while still trying desperately to reach his gun and hold the booby-trapped cover of the bomb in place, all at the same time.

And it wasn't until the first burst of automatic fire had stitched right across his chest that he finally dropped it, though I couldn't really blame him, could I?

Not when the one brain which controlled the two hands

158

was dead. Along with the rest of him.

I remember watching that rounded steel plate go skittering across the deck like a runaway dustbin lid while, all around it, the ricocheting shells sparked and slammed in a hellish frenzy of sound.

I remember thinking coldly, without any surprise or fear at all, 'Well, that's your bloody lot, Cable. All aboard f'r the ten mile ride right up to the top of the mushroom . . .' and feeling terribly sad for all the innocent people who were going to die within the next white-hot fragment of time. Because I knew that the remaining firing circuits within the bomb were already made as soon as the anti-tampering leads had been torn adrift.

I even remember thinking what a shame it was that McReadie hadn't been able to appreciate how well I was facing up to dying, now that it had come to our allotted time – then the firing stopped as abruptly as it had started and I could see that the Commander was still surprisingly alive and well and living in a little curled-up ball under the shelter of the starboard ladder. I knew that because he lifted his head and stared at me in stunned bewilderment, then spat, 'Where was our guard, Cable? You should've told me there wasn't any guard up there . . .'

Which meant it was my fault, as usual.

But that was the one small thing that annoyed me about McReadie. He was always such an impeccable bastard in his own eyes.

Then slowly – almost dispassionately – I started to realize something else. Something very odd indeed . . .

. . . That the bomb hadn't gone off after all.

While a coldly precise voice with only the slightest trace of an accent said from above us, 'Come out . . . Come where we can see you. And please – with your hands above your heads, *ja*.'

Completely ignoring the anonymous threat from above, McReadie still stared at me across the torn, bullet-riddled corpse of the late Ordnance Major Gray, and the expression of sheer agonized frustration on his features was something which I could really have enjoyed under any other circumstances – it was almost as if he was *annoyed* at not having been blown to charcoal scraps in the twinkling of an eye.

'It didn't *detonate*,' he muttered bitterly. 'The bloody thing hasn't gone up, an' he still hadn't finished rendering it harmless, had he?'

I glared back and thought what a damn silly thing to get needled about, especially with some kind of homicidal nut waiting right above us with a machine-gun . . . but it *was* peculiar, on reflection, though. Because I definitely remembered Gray emphasizing that *every* circuit had to be neutralized before that infernal cover plate could be separated. And what had he meant when, just before he'd died so suddenly, he'd made that obscure remark about, 'Now, at least, we have a little *time* . . .'

Then the hard voice above us stated indifferently, 'You have one minute to show yourselves. I repeat – one minute, precisely. Or we drop a grenade . . . do you understand?'

Oh, I understood all right. Even if it *was* for the first time that night. And anyway, I'd had enough, and I didn't give a damn any more, not about McReadie or BMSNC's crazy, impossible schemes or about all the killing that had taken place just so's we could wind up in a steel trap beside an atomic super-device that couldn't even atomize.

McReadie called urgently, 'Throw over your AK, Cable. I'll have a try for the bastards, whoever they are. Just a blind, hosepipe burst . . .'

I threw the gun down on the oily, blood-smeared plates and folded my hands over my head. 'Oh, get stuffed, McReadie!' I retorted tiredly, and stepped out into the glare of the overhead lights.

There were three of them up there, all dressed in belted black leather coats. The two on either side of the leader stood with legs stiffly apart and sub-machine-guns lowered so that the muzzles lined up unwaveringly with my tie. The other man leaned over the rail in an attitude of offering a sweetie to a child, except he held a grenade instead of a bar of chocolate but, when he saw me, the outstretched arm relaxed fractionally and with a quaint, old-fashioned gesture he clicked his heels like a true Teutonic gentleman.

'Permit me to introduce myself. My name is Geber. Horst Geber . . .'

I didn't feel surprise. In fact I hardly even felt resentment about being held up aboard my own ship, under the circumstances. The man above me must have had a king-sized chip on his shoulder, too, when he saw his dream of becoming Adolph Hitler's successor crumbling under the tracks of the Soviet T54s. And he must have understood why . . . or he wouldn't have been waiting for us.

And then he confirmed it.

'Your Task Force. There never was one, was there?'

I hesitated, then shook my head hopelessly. The kidding was over.

Geber gazed down at me expressionlessly but I saw the hand tremble as it gripped the grenade. Then he seemed to smile, almost as if he appreciated the joke. Only there wasn't any humour in it. Not even a little bit.

'Two victories for the price of one, perhaps? A spy ship returned to its government and the simultaneous extinction of an organization which could eventually prove . . . ah . . . morally embarrassing to your highly-principled NATO masters, shall we say?'

I winced. Whatever else he was, mini-*Führer* Geber was quick to catch on. But it also suggested something else – that he didn't know all of it. He still didn't guess our real reason for hijacking *Venturer*.

I interrupted quickly, 'I wouldn't know about motives, Geber. I'm only the paid hand around here!'

He eyed me reflectively for a moment, then gestured curtly. 'You will instruct the other man to join you in my sight. I should prefer our discussion to continue on a basis of mutual mistrust . . . but with my side commanding all the tactical advantages.'

I didn't need to tell McReadie anyway, he was already stepping awkwardly over Gray's body and, as I watched him, I was sad to see the bitter expression on his features. You see, that was the difference between him and me – he had a lot of hurt pride where I only had fear. And on top of that, the rounds which had smashed into the Major must have stroked him with the hot breath of their passing and that, even to an iceberg like McReadie, must have been a pretty traumatic happening.

But he still snarled, 'Heroic bastard!' at me, so he couldn't have changed all that much.

I turned back to Geber, anxious to steer the conversation away from *Venturer*. 'What about the rest of my men? I suppose you shot them in the bloody back as well, did you?'

'Not all of them. Not yet.'

'An' what's *that* supposed to mean?'

He ignored the question but I felt a surge of optimism that maybe some of the others were still alive, and that meant we could still try for getting out of here – if we could get rid of the Teutonic fly in our ointment first. Or was it more appropriate to think of him as a spider? The spider asked sharply, 'What are your names, ranks and functions in this particular operation?'

I hesitated. It wasn't that I was scared any more, it was just that I didn't believe in aggravating people who stood over me with hand grenades, not just for the hell of it. And I had to gain time, so I tried to avoid McReadie's warning eye. 'My name is Cable, Captain Brevet Cable. My function is to sail this ship out of here, nothing more.'

The gun barrels lined on my chest didn't even waver, and neither did Geber's eyes. He nodded and looked pleased. '*Gute!* Then you will continue in that capacity . . . only now I will be the paymaster and you will take your orders from me.'

'Orders?'

'You will still sail this ship as soon as possible, *Kapitän*. But you will take me with you as far as the Swedish coast. There you will land me and continue your voyage as before. You understand me?'

I chewed my lip and pretended to think. Oh, I understood him, all right. I'd continue a voyage without a doubt – but with a bullet in the back of the head. Geber just wasn't the type to forgive and forget. And there was another complication – in the fact that *Venturer* wasn't scheduled to steam as far as the Swedish coast . . .

. . . but that problem would come later, and now was now. Firstly I had to buy time. After a very small and presumably allowable gesture of protest.

I said toughly, 'What if I refuse, eh?'

The man above me shrugged. It was then that I noticed how cold his eyes were. 'Then you will be shot, *Kapitän*,' he answered with equally icy precision. 'Just once. In the groin. You will take rather a long time to die, I think.'

I thought so too. Only I'd rather been planning on an even longer lifespan ahead of me, like maybe another forty or fifty years. I spread my hands. 'You're on the passenger list as from now, Geber. What d'you want to . . .!'

'So you're gutless *and* naïve, Cable!' McReadie snarled dogmatically from behind. 'If you think that bastard's goin' to let us sail away after . . .'

I said, 'Excuse me?' to Geber and turned wearily to McReadie. I was getting just a little tired of this stiff-upper-lipped sneering in the face of death, apart from which I was a great believer in the philosophy of 'He who fights and runs away, lives . . . et cetera', and I'd suddenly found I wanted to live very desperately indeed. Which meant I had to stop McReadie shooting his suicidal British mouth off before he got us both killed for a principle.

So I hit him. Not hard, but pleasantly. Because I owed him that much for getting me into this bloody awful mess in the first place. The only real regret I had right then was that

J.C. wasn't there, too. In fact if he had been, then maybe I wouldn't have bothered covering-up – it would have been a pleasure and a privilege just to make up the set in front of a firing squad alongside that unmitigated, treble dyed, true blue ...

I blinked down, a bit pleased, at McReadie's suddenly dormant form and thought with some pride that I must have more strength than I realized. Then a strangely disquieting noise from above made me pivot to see, with astonishment, that the sound came from the mouth of Horst Geber. And that it meant he was actually *laughing*. In fact, even the two henchmen were smiling evilly like they'd just had their batteries switched on for a quick giggle . . . then I looked away and saw Gray's eviscerated corpse, and started to feel anger again. But also a bit of shame.

Geber good-humouredly jerked his chin at the unconscious Commander. 'Now there is a brave man. But not, perhaps, a trustworthy member of your crew, *ja*? For a man like that does not have enough fear for his life.'

'He's just had a man shot to death beside him, Geber,' I snapped, suddenly frightened for McReadie. 'That's enough to make anyone a bit cynical.'

And then I saw, or thought I saw, a movement above Geber. High up the ladders spiralling down to where we stood. For a moment my heart leapt hopefully, but then there was nothing. Simply the glare of the arc lamps and the static, unhelpful gleam of polished metal. Meanwhile Geber had stopped smiling so abruptly that I felt the tangible aura of madness emanating from him for the first time.

I probed tentatively, 'What about my crew, then? Including my Chief Engineer? If you've killed him you'd better start your boys rowing, *Führer*.'

I saw the eyes flicker nervously to where Gray was sprawled. Any moment now he was bound to start asking precisely what we were doing before they arrived, and giving the knowledge of our own private H-bomb to a nutter like Geber, even if it was a doubtful starter, could be

like sending out fifty megaton invitations to the massacre ...
I said quickly, 'He was just an electrical officer. We had a
minor fault in the windlass circuit ... the man I mean is my
Chief Engineer. He was on the control platform where you
are the last time I saw him. And I spoke to him from the
bridge only a few minutes before you nabbed him.'

I held my breath and hoped they knew as much about
ship repairs as they apparently did about starting successful
revolutions. Then I relaxed at the same time as he did.
'Not before, *Kapitän*, but *after*. He proved a barely adequate
conversationalist, even with a Luger placed against his
head ...'

Which accounted for Chief Reid's lack of enthusiasm on
the phone. I listened hopefully as Geber finished, '... he is
still alive, but just a little bit unconscious. We are really
very kind, *ja*?'

I didn't honestly know – maybe he should try asking
Major Gray. I probed a little harder. 'I need more men than
that. What about the others, like the ones who were on the
bridge? I had a navigating officer checking out the gear up
there.'

He shrugged. 'You will navigate anyway. But there are
several of your men now confined in a certain place on
deck. They were good soldiers but not difficult to surprise
... not when we were already on board and waiting for
you.' He smiled briefly, 'You British do not have the
advantage of the experience we have gained over twenty-
five years of practical subversion ...'

I tried not to look relieved, but I still had to know
about young Twist. 'How many then? How many did you
kill?'

'Only one. On the bridge. He was very violent. He
balanced the account for my man, the one you killed when
you came aboard.'

I closed my eyes and remembered Colour Sergeant
Lattice. And the cheesewire collar. But it sounded as though
I still had a team, even if I didn't have any illusions that

Geber hadn't been so much merciful as practical. Temporarily.

Then Geber leaned over fractionally, still trying to see what we had been doing before they'd killed Gray, and I hurriedly blurted out the first thing which came into my head. 'Kleiber. And all those other poor bastards dying for you out there . . . Don't you feel any responsibility to them, Geber?'

For a moment I thought I'd pushed my luck too far, but I had to distract him. Any suggestion that I was still trying to conceal anything would mean a hail of bullets while every minute of life gained offered a slim chance of turning the tables – hell, I think that was the moment when I even had the first germ of an idea for taking *Venturer* into deep water and then – instead of landing a retired revolutionary – just blowing the guts out of her as originally planned.

Only that was strictly for heroes. Like McReadie down there. And he was still unconscious.

Geber simply shrugged though. 'Their responsibility was to me, Cable. To me and the Fourth Reich. And because they have failed they will pay the penalty – precisely as the German people who abandoned Adolph Hitler in his hour of need should have paid . . . Kleiber and his scum? I would welcome the privilege of executing every last one of them myself!'

'You appreciative bastard!' I thought savagely. 'You an' J.C. would get on well together . . .' And then McReadie groaned and stirred while I hoped to God *he* wasn't going to come round and start screwing everything up. I even thought about kicking him on his already battered and stubborn skull but I didn't really want to anymore. We were square again, now, and I still liked him a lot.

I gestured to the ladder hopefully. 'I navigate better if I can see where I'm going, Geber. And you've got a Chief Engineer to resurrect unless you want to charter a Soviet tugboat, so if I could just come up . . .'

I had one foot on the ladder when he said, '*Nein!*'

166

For a moment I just stood there and tried to stop myself from breaking down completely. This time I really had reached the end of my tether. Then I took a last, deep breath of courage and snarled irritably, 'Oh f'r cryin' out loud, man! How can I . . .'

'Exactly my point, *Herr Kapitän.* How *can* you?'

I blinked. Somewhere along the line we'd slipped on to a different frequency. 'What, Geber? How can I what?'

The blue eyes bored into me. 'Prove your intentions, Cable. How can you convince me that all your glib talk isn't just another British confidence trick and that you won't just take this ship to sea and then, perhaps, run her on the rocks. Or scuttle her in some way that I could not know of.'

The nervous tic came back for the first time since Gray had died. I didn't dare look up for the fear that he would see the guilt in my eyes. Or had he known all the time that no British agent could be quite as co-operative as I'd pretended to be? Which could mean that this was just a bloody evil game of cat and mouse – maybe to square the ledger for what he must have gone through while he watched his mad dream of a new Germany crumble away under a blaze of Soviet gunfire?

I bit my lip and stared hard at the diagonal pattern etched on the ladder treads in front of me. 'All right, then suppose you *tell* me how, Geber?'

He licked his lips, looking almost like a little boy with a good idea. A hungry, greedy little boy. And then I remembered a phrase from my discussion with the man from the Department of Strategic Studies, when he was describing the megalomaniac above me. He'd said, '. . . *a man of considerable and varied appetites.*'

Like sadism, for instance? Because it was suddenly there, a tangible quality, in his voice.

As he said slowly but with barely controlled excitement, 'I have a pistol here, my friend. There will be only one bullet in the magazine, you understand?'

I suppose I must have guessed what was coming, but I still didn't believe it. I just heard myself dimly answering, 'Yeah. I understand.'

'*Das gute!* Then the way you can persuade me – and it is the only certain way, *Kapitän* – that you are a true self-seeker and not merely a very convincing liar, is to use that one bullet . . .'

The lights seemed to go dim.

'. . . when you place the muzzle of the gun in your comrade's mouth. And pull the trigger!'

And it was then that I knew I was going to kill McReadie.

Because I had to.

Oh, I thought hard about the alternatives, by God but I did. For instance I even thought about putting it to my own head and at least having the last laugh on both Geber *and* J.C. But it didn't really appeal all that much to my somewhat depleted sense of humour and, anyway, they'd still have shot McReadie before I'd hit the deck.

Or I could have given myself a treat by expending the round on *Führer* Geber's belt buckle. But that would have made him a proper martyr and, apart from that, there was still only the one bullet, which meant McReadie would still have died right alongside me half a Fallschirmjaeger magazine later . . . and even *that* presupposed there really was an actual live round in the gun, and that this wasn't just a gigantic but fraudulent test of my true determination, without any real risk to Geber.

But the real reason I decided McReadie had to go was behind that exposed wiring panel over there. That bloody awful weapon – Because I suddenly knew that J.C. had been right all the time, and that we could never hazard our secret of perpetrating an indetectable thermo-nuclear pre-emptive strike. So I had to destroy the bomb, and *British Venturer* along with it, and doing that would undoubtedly mean killing myself and everyone else aboard anyway. Which only meant that McReadie would be meeting my one-legged, phantom captain just a little earlier than the rest of us . . .

Geber said flatly, but with a lot of menace, 'Well?'

'Give me the gun.'

He suddenly sounded a bit surprised and excited.

'Then you *do* intend to . . .?'

I swung round and shouted, 'Give me the bloody GUN!'

Easy, Cable. Killing a friend isn't supposed to be hard, not for the kind of man you're pretending to be. Not for a man who wants to stay alive at any price . . .

The gun skittered across the deck plates at my feet. Slowly I bent down and picked it up, hefting it experimentally. It was a nine millimetre Browning High Power automatic, manufactured under Belgian licence. I could see the stamping along the blued, square- cutbarrel – *Fabrique Nationale D'Armes De Guerre. Herstal. Belgique* . . . It was a good gun. I knew McReadie would appreciate that much.

There was a slight shuffling above me and I looked up to see that the two Nazi gunmen had moved forward tensely, colandered gun barrels now lined very nervously on my chest. It proved that one of my faint hopes for McReadie didn't exist – it proved that the gun I held was, without any shadow of a doubt, loaded.

I slipped the safety catch off.

And knelt down beside McReadie with the vomit bitter in my mouth.

Then he opened his eyes. Which meant he must know exactly what was going to happen . . .

Oh, merciful *Christ*!

Suddenly I didn't care whether Geber heard me or not – but I still only whispered, all the same. 'I promise, Mac. I swear it's not for . . .'

'. . . yourself?' He closed his eyes again and I saw a wispy shadow of the old McReadie grin. Except his lips were bloodless white slits in the grey face.

'I know,' he muttered, and I had to bend forward slightly before I could even hear him. 'I know now why you're

doing it, Brev. But do it quick. Ever so bloody quick .
please?'

I started to cry softly. The trigger felt very cold against my
forefinger.

I'd never realized before just how much noise a Browning
automatic could make – firing in such an enclosed space.

Except that it couldn't have been *my* Browning automatic.
Not when the burst must have been all of twenty rounds
long . . .

Really, it was very unfair.

I mean the way the open, dead eyes stared into mine with
such an expression of shocked disbelief that, just for a moment,
I started to shout hysterically, 'But I haven't even *fired*, f'r
Chrissake! An' anyway, you knew what I had to do,
McReadie! You bloody said you *knew* . . .!'

Then I slammed back in horrified revulsion, and blinked
uncomprehendingly at a corpse who couldn't possibly be
speaking to me because the whole of its jaw and most of the
mouth had been shot away.

Yet McReadie's voice was still screaming excitedly, 'The
gun, Cable! Oh, gimme the bloody gun . . .!'

Then someone or other fired again. Which was even more
confusing than the first time. Especially as they couldn't be
shooting at either McReadie or me . . .

. . . until something big, flailing and squashy hit the plates
beside me with a sickening thud and – all of a sudden – I
was gazing down at *two* bullet riddled cadavers. And the
oddest factor of all was that they were both wearing what
must have been black leather coats once. Before the first
three dozen shells or so had altered the cut of the skins. And
the colour.

I looked up at the platform and frowned. Things had
changed a bit up there, as well, because now Geber wasn't
looking down at me with that evil gleam any longer. No, he
now seemed a lot more interested in something behind him.
Something I couldn't see for the angle of the engine-room

ladder, but which undoubtedly worried my own private megalomaniac butcher a lot more than the current loyalties of Captain Brevet Cable, M.N.

He backed up against the rail and held out his hands pleadingly. '*Nein! . . . Nein kamerad?*'

Beside me someone started yelling urgently, 'LEAVE him! Hold your fire 'cause we need him back at . . .' and I looked round and saw it was a still very much alive McReadie. And I couldn't really understand it all yet, but I *did* know that whoever it was with the sub machine-gun up there had cut down the two Nazi bodyguards less than the blink of a dead man's eye before *I'd* been able to fire my solitary round. Which made me feel all pleasant and warm inside, because I liked McReadie such a lot, even if it had needed my having to kill him first to prove it.

Geber screamed disbelievingly, '*Nein! Nichts weniger als* . . .'

Then the first rounds of the third calculated burst took him right in the pit of the stomach, slamming him over into a hunched-up, foetal attitude of supplication.

McReadie said irritably, 'Oh, *bugger* it!' while I just stared up at the collapsing man above me and thought: 'What a funny thing to say when you're watching a murder.' Until the Commander's hand gripped my shoulder and hauled me to one side just in time.

As the invisible gun racketed again and the already dead symbol of the Fourth Reich was hammered jerkily through the eighteen-inch gap between the rails of the platform to tumble – rather poetically, I felt – beside the body of Ordnance Major Gray.

I looked at McReadie and he looked at me, and I knew he really had understood. Tentatively I handed him the Browning and he stared thoughtfully at it for quite a long time. Then he threw it down with a funny, almost disbelieving shudder, and we both waited for the man who'd just deposed a not very effective *Führer* to turn the corner.

Strong teeth flashed briefly against a blackened, sweat-streaked face before he saluted in a very smart and very British manner. Which was possibly the strangest thing that had happened all night in a way.

Coming, as it did, from *Hauptmann* Paulus Kleiber, lately of *Wiedereinstellung Armee-Oberkommando*.

Now disbanded!

Eight

I stood out on the high wing of *Venturer*'s bridge, silently gazing across the roofs of the wharf buildings and listening to the sporadic crackle of small arms fire which still carried occasionally over the otherwise passive city.

Something was burning to the east, a long way away, and I wondered if the sirens I could hear were those of the civil powers – or had even the firemen joined in the last suicidal frenzy of resistance? Either way our luck couldn't hold very much longer. At any moment the headlights of a Soviet personnel carrier could swing on to the quay, checking out their prize propaganda exhibit. And there was now a trail of gunned-down corpses below which would lead them straight to an already conveniently – and quite miraculously – disarmed and dormant bomb . . .

It was time to go. And fast!

I swung round to see Twist stepping out of the wheel-house, his face a white blob in the darkness. We'd switched the cargo lamps off a few minutes ago, then waited tensely for any sounds of those curiously investigating patrols. And there was still time for them to arrive yet.

The Second Mate – I still thought of Twist as a Second, he seemed so young and fresh – said quietly, 'Singled up fore and aft, sir. And Mister Reid on stand-by down below.'

I nodded. 'Commander McReadie up forr'ad, is he?'

'Yessir. And Lieutenant De'Ath on the poop . . . I'll take the wheel and the Corporal can handle the telegraphs and docking phones just now.'

I took a deep breath, feeling the deck vibrating gently beneath my feet. So we were finally all set to go. All ready for *Venturer*'s last, one-destination voyage. And she felt so damnably good, being a real, living ship once more. I didn't know how I was going to bring myself to sink her in cold blood. But then if those Soviet Fleet Units intercepted us again I wouldn't have to. They'd do it all for me because, this time, we couldn't afford to stop and let them take us, not while there was one of us left alive to keep her steaming defiantly towards deep water.

Inconsequentially I thought of Kleiber and couldn't help smiling a bit. It was ironic, really – the way he'd returned aboard to rejoin his beloved *Führer*, only to hear Geber's wistful reflection on how much satisfaction he'd get out of personally shooting *Hauptmann* Paulus Kleiber in the back of the head.

I just hoped J.C. would learn something from it. A kind of moral fable about what happened to people who lacked proper appreciation for the efforts of their subordinates.

If we ever got home to stress the point in the first place.

And then there'd been the shamefaced, embarrassing bit. The hasty freeing of the rest of the OPERATION STAYSAIL crowd from where they'd been held in the steel box of the centre-castle bosun's store. While McReadie and I had watched dead-pan, and Kleiber with a sort of pleased smirk on his face, as young Twist had stumbled uncertainly back to where it was all happening, followed by De'Ath – red with mortification and dried blood from the vicious gash on his forehead – and my Marine Corporal who just glared at everybody in turn in a hurt, aggressively petulant way and muttered bitterly, 'Fuckin' screwed up as usual! Fuckin' Merchant Navy . . . Fuckin' *recruitin'* officers.'

It proved he'd never worked for J.C. and the British Mutual Steam Navigation Company before. Or else he'd have been used to it by now. Like me . . .

I called, 'Let go forr'ad.'

A tiny blip of light from the bows. McReadie hadn't wasted time, he'd just let the rope run through the fairleads and into the black water below. But we wouldn't be needing mooring lines ever again. I leant out over the wing and

174

faced the stern. 'Leggo aft!'

A moment's hesitation. 'C'mon, come *on*, De'Ath . . .'

'All gone aft, sir.'

'Slow ahead starboard. Port twenty the wheel.'

The telegraphs jangled from the wheelhouse and I winced. Damn! Should've remembered those bells, muffled them somehow. Twist spun the wheel hard then called softly, 'Wheel's twenty to port, sir.'

'Ease to ten. Slow ahead port engine.'

A quick glance over the wing, down at the sluggishly moving ink below and at the quayside already fading astern into the darkness. A green flare went up a long way away, followed immediately by a renewed frenzy of firing. Then a T54 gun slammed and I caught the momentary glow of phosphorescence before it fell away below the line of the rooftops. So the dying hadn't quite finished yet? But I didn't really mind – we needed thirty more minutes of grace to get out of the estuary and out into the Baltic. And it sort of detracted from other people's problems, when you had to act as chauffeur to a thermo-nuclear doom machine.

Hell! The bows were swinging too fast to port, nearly on to our first course line to clear the red flashing spark of the buoy marking the fairway. And all I needed right now was to run *Venturer* as hard aground as an oak tree in a desert, and in full view of the already trigger-happy custodians of Ahldenstadt.

I called urgently, 'Midships the wheel . . . Meet her!'

'Wheel's amidships . . .'

The swing of the bow slowed, then stopped with the jackstay cutting half a point to the side of the distant buoy. Bloody good, Twist. '. . . Steady on two seven eight, sir.'

'Nothing to port.'

'Nothing to port. Aye, aye, sir.'

The wind gradually started to curl over the canvas dodgers and I lifted my face to feel its clean breath. It smelt of the sea, and that meant freedom – even if there were rather too many Red warships out there with other ideas.

Plus a radar defence screen fanning out from the East German and Polish coasts which would follow and plot us as soon as we steamed clear of the land clutter. But there were a lot of ships in the Baltic, and all of them unidentifiable blips on the same screen. It had to be a case of losing ourselves in a crowd.

If we ever made it as far as the crowd in the first place.

A movement behind me and I turned jumpily to see McReadie. He nodded towards the line of buoys marking the main channel, all flashing and occulting in an apparently crazy jumble of coloured cautions. 'D'you know where you're going?'

I remembered that we didn't have any recent corrections to the old charts we carried, and that Ahldenstadt was a compulsory pilotage area anyway, but still kept my voice deliberately indifferent. 'No. Do you?'

He grinned. 'No.'

'Then you shut up an' I'll drive the boat my way.'

I leant over the bridge front and stared happily ahead. It was back to normal between me and McReadie and it felt good. He was silent for a few moments then he glanced up and saw our radar scanner whirling monotonously above the softly rumbling funnel.

'You know they can pick up our radar transmission like we were waving a flag, don't you?'

I shrugged. 'Along this coast everybody employs radar. Without it we'd be like a eunuch at an orgy – people would notice if we weren't using ours.'

The first buoy came abeam, a froth of white water tailing down-river from it with the stream. I stepped over to the wheelhouse and called, 'Come five more to starboard, Mister. Steady on two eight thuree . . . Half ahead both.'

Chewing my bottom lip nervously I stared ahead through the windows as the bows swung slightly and steadied. We were in the main channel now and, so far, there hadn't been any indication that we'd been missed from our berth. There was a slight cough from behind and I turned to see Twist

176

glancing hesitantly at me over the binnacle, the light picking out his features eerily as he spoke. 'It'll be daylight in another forty minutes, sir. Then they'll see us for sure.'

Nodding I did a quick calculation in my head. We still had another twenty-five minutes to run down to the Fairway Buoy at this speed, which only gave us fifteen minutes at full ahead to get clear of the land and any casual observer. Which meant we'd be less than five miles out by the time we were Exhibit 'A' for every amateur coastguard along the East German shore. And, while I'd been banking on the fact that the Soviet radar stations wouldn't yet have been alerted to look for any *outgoing* ships, *British Venturer* was still a natural for a visual identification by anyone who'd read the papers recently . . .

McReadie came in behind me and asked, 'What's wrong, Brev?'

I rubbed my eyes tiredly. 'This bloody ship, that's what's wrong. We're so obviously British we should have a bulldog an' a teapot flying at the masthead. Hell, they only need to look up our funnel livery to place our origin . . .'

He said briskly, 'So what other colour would you like? McReadie's Contractors are now open for business.'

I stared at him. 'You must be kidding, pal. It's nearly dawn now. Painting that funnel's like tackling a gasometer with a toothbrush!'

'What *colour*? There's me, De'Ath, four Marines plus the two assault engineers . . .' he grinned cynically, '. . . and *Herr Hauptmann* Kleiber.'

I gave in wearily. 'How about black then? It's a good colour, black is. For funnels or for bloody funerals. And Kleiber'd like it – maybe it'll remind him of home.'

They took exactly seventeen minutes to convert us from a cargo liner of the British Mutual Steam Navigation Company to a black-liveried, anonymous freighter with a Panamanian Ensign and a very unseamanlike, paint-splattered boat-deck. It made me a bit ashamed in a way, because I was still house-proud of *Venturer*. But then again – painting from a five gallon palette with a broom head wasn't a technique that Rembrandt used all that often either.

McReadie even struck out our name and port of registry as well. Just in case anyone on shore had a really high powered pair of binoculars to go with an inquisitive yen for maritime meddling.

It wasn't terribly important – on reflection – but I suppose it was better for morale than just letting them hang about waiting for something to happen.

Which – when it did – just had to be something nasty.

I couldn't believe it. Things were actually going right, at last.

In fact we didn't see another ship all the way down to the Fairway Buoy. I just leant on the rail and sweated it out, and watched the dawn-tinged outline of the tormented city fade astern until, finally, we rounded the point of the estuary and felt the Baltic swell lifting our bows with an almost light-hearted bound of sheer exhilaration.

Though the ship couldn't really have been feeling very happy, not in the knowledge that I was going to kill her in another two hours and ten minutes. I blinked at the red flashing light ahead and lit a Capstan. She was *my* ship, my very first command . . . I gradually stopped feeling scared and just started feeling sad instead.

McReadie came back up to the bridge looking a bit paint-spattered and stood silently beside me as we came abeam of the last, tangible reminder of Ahldenstadt. I flicked the stub of my cigarette over the end of the wing and watched as it fell away into the rushing water along our hull. McReadie said quietly, 'Thinking, Brev? What're you thinking about?'

He'd said exactly the same thing that time so long ago, when we'd stood up here on *Venturer*'s bridge for the first time, and I'd been so proud and happy because she was mine. But now they were taking her from me for ever, and I knew I would never forgive them for that.

So I just muttered, 'Oh, why don't you go an' blow

something up, Commander? Like the whole fucking world!'

But I didn't really mean it to happen. Not in the way that it turned out.

'Steer oh four five degrees. Aye, aye, sir.'

Twist spun the wheel and I felt the ship heel over fractionally as we swung round to our final heading towards deep water. I glanced at my watch – 07.00 hours – but there was still a lot of sea to cover. Nearly an hour's steaming until we were past the twenty fathom line when every turn of the screw from then on would mean another few feet shrouding *Venturer*'s eviscerated carcase when we finally blew the double bottoms out of her.

'Steady on oh four five, sir.'

'Thank you.'

I wondered how McReadie and the Marine assault engineers were progressing down below. They should have had enough time to lay their charges and wire them for simultaneous detonation by now. De'Ath had said the time fuses were pre-set to give us twenty minutes' grace to abandon ship and get clear . . . Please, God, just let that submarine be waiting at the rendezvous and not let her commander be too impatient. We were late now, because of Geber, hell of a late. The pick-up had been scheduled for now – 07.00 hours – but there was still another twenty miles. Nearly an hour's steaming.

I bent over the radar screen again and tried to forget the problem of what to do while we were left floating around the Baltic in a lifeboat while the Navy was on its way home for breakfast without us. For starters we were still well inside Red waters and *they* would be more than pleased to rescue us instead. Except that they might have a few queries to make about the Ahldenstadt massacre, and who had instigated it in the first place . . .

Much the same pattern on the screen as five minutes ago. One big ship just over the horizon, heading east, presumably to Gdynia or Gdansk. Which meant she was probably under the Soviet or Polish flags. A few smaller blips over to starboard which could be fishing boats. I twisted the range control and a large, rounded coastline took shape to the north – the island of Bornholm. Just pray, Cable, that if you have to row, then you make it to there before the Reds pick you up.

The engine-room phone shrilled abruptly across the silence of the wheelhouse. It was so unexpected that I must have jumped an involuntary three feet in the air, but I wasn't alone with my runaway nervous reflexes – I saw Twist watching me over the wheel with apprehensively bright eyes as I snatched the receiver off its hook.

'Bridge.'

McReadie's voice, distorted above the pounding background roar of the diesels. 'Better get down here, Cable! You'd better get down here right away.'

I virtually stopped breathing for a moment as a cold premonition hit me with almost physical shock. Then partly for young Twist's benefit I recovered myself savagely. 'Oh f'r Chrissake, McReadie. You know I can't leave the bri . . .'

He shouted, 'Jus' you geddown here *now*, Cable . . . while you've still got a bridge to bloody leave!'

The phone went dead as he slammed the receiver back on its hook and I was left staring dazedly at my end of it. The fear had come back even worse than before, because we'd been through a lot of terrible things that night already and – now we were finally on the last, nerve-racking lap – I just couldn't face up to any more problems.

And it couldn't be the bomb, not now. Because the bomb was dead, just like Ordnance Major Gray, and I knew that much because *we* were still alive to prove it. And even if it had, quite ridiculously, gone wrong then McReadie certainly wouldn't have had time to phone . . . so what *was* he sounding so choked about?

I steeled myself and gestured casually to the Second Mate. 'Probably nothing, Mister. Just keep her on that heading and I'll be back in a few minutes.'

His eyes followed me all the way across the wing as I forced myself to walk slowly and unconcernedly towards the ladder – and it wasn't until I'd reached the boat-deck that I started running like a maniac sprinter.

I met Kleiber pulling himself up the prom-deck ladders and, when he saw me coming, he looked a bit disconcerted about the obvious instability of British ship's masters who seemed to spend all their time in command just building up a high-speed mileage around the boat.

He called tentatively, 'Ah, *Herr Kapitän* Cable. I should like to . . .' then I hauled him out of the way and yelled over my shoulder, 'Later, Kleiber. A lot bloody later . . .' And carried on running while feeling a bit of a bastard because Kleiber still thought he was travelling to freedom First Class when, instead, he was just scheduled for a lifeboat ride while we blew the bottom out of his liberty ship.

McReadie was waiting for me on the control platform. Even from the top of the ladder I could see he looked grim-faced and worried and I started wishing I'd taken a few obvious precautions. Like bringing my lifejacket, or even a gun in case they'd flushed another nest of Nazis while they were laying the charges . . .

The charges? It just had to be . . . Oh, *Jesus*!

I skidded to a halt in front of him and shouted wildly, 'You've made a cock-up with the charge settings, haven't you? An' now you're goin' to tell me the whole damn operation's . . .'

He snapped, 'It's not the charges, Cable!'

I blinked at him for a moment, feeling a bit hysterical, while he repeated again, 'No, it's not the charges, Cable – it's that goddamn bomb! It's still alive after all . . .'

I stared at him in disbelief. He looked very white under his tan. '. . . I think the firing mechanism has activated itself. It could detonate at any minute.'

I pleaded, 'You *are* kidding, McReadie . . . aren't you?'

He said flatly, 'No!'

I looked at him almost hatefully. 'But it's a hydrogen bomb

f'r Chris . . . I mean it just *can't* go off here. Not in this part of the world? Things jus' don't bloody well happen like that for real.'

I suppose that, deep down, I'd never really believed that the nightmare could ever become fact. Maybe it was just because of the scale of the thing – the explosion of a torpèdo or a grenade, or the smashing impact of a nine millimetre bullet – those things I could grasp. They were tangible and, consequently, terrifying in their possibility. But a thermo-nuclear super holocaust? Where a man standing twenty miles away could feel his eyeballs actually melting with the heat, and the blast would flatten a multi-storey block at thirty miles . . .

I couldn't really *be* ordinary scared. Not of that. Because once you started to credit the possibility of a horror on that scale, then you just gave up living and existed in a twilight world of fear and loathing for what tomorrow would bring.

I heard myself saying quietly, 'How d'you know, Mac? That it's due to blow?'

He turned away urgently and I followed him down the ladder to the bulkhead where the guts of the Thing still lay exposed from when Gray had died so violently. Oh, they'd removed the bodies but it didn't really matter – not if McReadie was right – because we had the biggest crematorium in the world right at our disposal. And undoubtedly for our own personal use as well.

De'Ath and the Marine AEs were there, and the Chief, all watching silently as I crouched down to look at the stamped panel with its surrounding necklace of metal studs and the broken, dangling ends of the wires Gray just never had time to neutralize. There wasn't very much to see, come to that, and I certainly couldn't hear if it was ticking or whatever because the roar of the flat-out diesels made even shouting difficult to hear.

I made a querying gesture to McReadie and yelled, nervously irritable, 'So what makes you think it's all systems go, then?'

He still didn't say anything. He just knelt down beside me and unsnapped a narrow, top-hinged oblong metal cover above the fuse panel. I blinked disconcertedly, nobody had ever told me it even existed.

They hadn't told me what the numerical counter behind it was for, either. But the thing which gave me a really funny, unsettled feeling in the pit of my stomach was what the counter was doing – and why.

Because it was steadily and remorselessly counting down. And I knew immediately, without any doubt whatsoever, that every tick was one scientifically precise second nearer to the end.

I muttered, 'Oh, Lord!' But it wasn't so much of a blasphemy this time as an appeal.

McReadie grated savagely, 'An' *He* can't help much, either. Not unless He knows His nuclear physics.'

The counter continued counting.

I got down on my hands and knees and examined it, oddly aware with mixed feelings that I wasn't frightened anymore. Not now it was really happening. Perhaps it was just that my mind still couldn't comprehend the vast horror of it all, or maybe I'd had my saturation dose of fear for that night, and that my consciousness just couldn't absorb any further sensory stimulation. Or something.

There appeared to be two sets of figures. The left hand row – the white ones – read *Zero Two Six One* . . . blast this bloody light! That's better . . . *Niner!* So if I discount the first zero that gives a white reading of two thousand, six hundred and nineteen. Check! And they haven't altered, not since I first saw them a few moments ago . . . But the goddamned red ones to the right have! Only two digits . . . *Zero Six*. But *that*'s changing all the time . . .

. . . *Zero Five. Zero Four. Zero* bloody *Three* . . .

Zero Zero.

And, all of a sudden, the meter only read two thousand, six hundred and *eighteen* white. With red fifty-nine . . . fifty-eight . . . fifty-seven . . .

183

I looked at my watch. The time was 7.26 a.m.

And suddenly I knew the answer. I knew the exact time that *British Venturer* was scheduled to evaporate in a white-hot mushroom cloud.

It was very peaceful up on the bridge again, after all the heat and noise of the engine-room.

I'd just forced myself to grin reassuringly at young Twist as I arrived with McReadie, and had a good look round the still empty horizon coupled with a quick glance into the radar scan which confirmed that – rather surprisingly for the Baltic – we were relatively alone in an empty sea. Which also proved what a brilliant strategist *I* was when I theorized about losing ourselves in a crowd. But the Reds hadn't come looking for us yet, so it didn't really matter and besides – we now had a helluva lot more to worry about than a few common-or-garden uncomplicated warships.

And so had the warships, if they only but knew it.

I gestured McReadie out to the wing of the bridge and, without caring, said brutally, 'She's due to blow at around quarter to five, McReadie . . . at quarter to five the morning *after* tomorrow! And God help anyone within a fifty mile radius of here.'

He frowned gloomily at me. 'How d'you . . . ?'

'Look! Gray once told me that the bomb had a delayed action trigger – that the firing sequence could be activated but the final fusion process wouldn't take place for forty-eight hours. You understand?'

He shrugged. 'Maybe! But how d'you know it's that particular phase we're in now? There were a lot of alternative remote-firing methods built into the bloody thing . . .'

I slammed my hand down on the bridge rail. 'Oh f'r God's sake, McReadie! All I know was that she would either trigger off immediately – like she should have done the moment Gray ripped that panel away too prematurely –

184

or that she can explode at any time within the forty-eight hours. But the meter down there *must* have a bearing on exactly when.'

He bit his lip thoughtfully. 'So you reckon it's counting down to zero?'

'Yeah! In minutes and seconds . . . But listen hard. I checked my watch when the counter read two six wun eight on the white – the minute – digits. The time then was seven twenty-six, right?'

'Check!'

I took a deep breath and tried to force my brain to work logically which, in itself, was quite an undertaking for me. 'As near as I can place it, the Major got hit at between four-thirty and five a.m. Which means that, up to the time I read the meter, approximately two and three-quarter hours had passed . . . or one hundred an' sixty-five minutes.'

'So?'

'So what's forty-eight hours in minutes?'

McReadie frowned again but I could see that, behind all the cynicism, he was following me very keenly indeed. He said tentatively, 'Two thousand, eight hundred and . . . eighty?'

I forced a weak grin. 'You get the big cigar . . . Now. What d'you have left if you subtract the minutes elapsed from Gray's estimated time of death until when we looked at the meter – that one sixty-five?'

'. . . Two thousand, six . . . fifteen.'

I lit a cigarette and passed him one, blowing the smoke in a thin, vanishing streamer. '. . . and the meter read twenty six *eighteen*. Only three digits out, Mac . . . I've got to be right.'

He looked at me tightly. 'Which confirms what you say – this ship explodes the day after tomorrow. At early breakfast time.'

Neither of us spoke again for a few moments. I just stood there with the wind fingering my hair and thoughts racing crazily around my head. And they were all about people, innocent people, who lived not very far from here, and who wouldn't even know why – when they half turned to see what the glare in the sky was – and it suddenly reached over the horizon to touch them with death . . .

McReadie said hopelessly, 'What the hell do we *do*, Brev? Even with the forty-five hours we've got left?'

I glanced at my watch again. 7.40 a.m. And we were now less than half an hour's steaming from our delayed rendezvous with the submarine. I muttered bitterly, 'Maybe if we sink her as planned she won't really detonate. Not with thirty or forty fathoms over her.'

He looked at me and I knew there wasn't a hope. Not even enough to satisfy my selfish conscience. Not after what Gray had told me all that time ago about what the bomb could do, even if we did drown it. I leant over the rail and watched the sea racing along our high sides, feeling the throb of the engines as they drove us nearer and nearer to a very easy way out for Cable . . . aboard an *Oberon* Class submarine which would be well into the North Sea before that awful horror down below finally detonated . . .

McReadie said, 'We could take her further east? Say midway between Gotland and the Gulf of Danzig. Create a bigger margin of safety.'

I shook my head. 'The Baltic'll be solid with Soviet patrols down there. And even if we made it that far we'd still only have fifty, maybe sixty miles between us and the nearest coast . . . It's not enough, McReadie. Not nearly enough.'

Lucky, lucky Navy! In the North Sea they'd only hear the bang . . .

The North *Sea*.

I swung round on McReadie. 'There's no choice. We've got to take her out of the Baltic altogether, Mac. Right through the Kattegat, the Skagerrak and into the North Sea . . . where there's room for her to blow.'

He stared at me. 'You're out of your tiny mind, Cable. This is a floating time bomb and we don't even know for sure when she'll go up. But if she triggered off before we got out through the Öresund . . . Christ, man, we'd take Copenhagen, Malmö and half of Denmark an' Sweden up with us!'

I gripped his shoulder desperately. 'McReadie, I *know* I'm right – About the metering. Don't ask me how, but I just do . . . and think about the alternative. Either we try for further easting and almost certainly get arrested by a Soviet destroyer . . . or we actually make it to the Gotland-Danzig line and still kill and mutilate maybe half a million people along the Polish and Russian coasts when she goes up. Or of course there's the other way, the real punter's way . . . I could go down there, down below, and try to remove that last fuse. If you have a real yen for dicing with a lot of poor bloody innocents' futures.'

He shook his head. 'You can't. It's not a viable risk, Cable, not tampering any more with the thing.'

'I agree. But running for the North Sea *is*, man – 'cause doing it my way means that there's at least a possibility of being well away from any coastline when it happens.'

McReadie gripped the rail and I could see his knuckles white under the tan. He muttered, 'There's still a hell of a lot of shipping there. God help those hundreds of passenger ferries and coastermen, and the shorthaul traders . . .'

I said, 'All right. So we'll head north round the Naze. Right up into the Norwegian Sea . . .' I stopped short. It really was bloody ironic, when you came to think of it. '. . . Right back up to where it all started, McReadie. Right back up to where Pritytsky lost his leg . . .'

He looked at me in a funny way. Uncomprehending. 'Where *who* did what?'

I shook my head. I couldn't really have expected him to remember details. Because he hadn't been living with a ghost for a long time now, like me. 'Nothing,' I whispered softly. 'It's just someone I seem to know very well indeed.'

He took a deep breath and swung towards the wheel-house. 'Bring her round to due west, Mister Twist,' he said heavily. 'Until we can give you a course for Copenhagen Sound.'

I tried not to think of what would happen to all of us aboard *Venturer* when we finally got up into the Norwegian Sea. Because there wasn't going to be a submarine waiting for us there.

And we'd need every minute we could get, anyway. To beat that counter down below . . .

There are shipping lanes clearly defined in the Baltic. Well, in the Western end at least. They were originally the swept routes cleared by the mine counter-measures flotillas after the last war, and virtually all shipping uses them still. Just in case.

We didn't.

Instead we swung around in a tight, swaying arc and steadied on two nine five degrees true, then went like a bat out of hell for the Falsterborev Light. And maybe we were, at that – Something out of hell, I mean.

We entered the Sound about noon on the first day. We had averaged over twenty-four knots. I followed up Route Thirty-Two then, but it was only because I didn't have any choice, not until we'd steamed through the dense traffic of the Öresund and out into the Kattegat itself.

I think the pilotage authorities in Copenhagen must have been a little put out to watch us rampaging through their waters without even a request for one of their excellent gentlemen to guide us. But conning a ten thousand ton freighter at twenty-four knots through there *is* a bit like steering a steamroller at sixty down a pedestrian precinct, and I didn't think the Danish pilots would agree to try it.

Plus the fact that Marine Colour sergeants are inclined to bleed rather profusely when they're decapitated, and my once snowy bridge planking had developed a nasty, in-eradicable stain. And that might have struck a visiting pilot as a little odd, too.

188

But it looked nice, did Copenhagen, as we raced past in the sunlight. I should very much have loved to sit over a beer with McReadie in front of Fascati's, just around the corner from the Tivoli Gardens, then maybe wandered through the busy streets as far as Kongens Nytorv and the more disreputable sailors' bars of Nyhavn.

But all that took time.

And the counter said we only had two thousand, four hundred and seventy-six minutes left.

We charged through the narrowest part of the Öresund with every rivet in *Venturer* leaping and rattling in a pounding frenzy of mechanical hysteria. I remember seeing the squat silvery rows of oil tanks on the Swedish shore in strange contemporary contrast to the black towering bulk of Helsingor's Kronborg Castle – Shakespeare's Elsinore of legendary fame.

I'd grinned a bit cynically just then, when I remembered they had a king over there, once, who used to stop and levy a tax on every ship entering or leaving the Baltic. His name was Eric of Pomerania and he'd been a bit like the Russians in a funny sort of way.

He'd installed the biggest battery of cannons in the world to use when negotiation failed.

Things hadn't really changed a lot since 1426. Apart from the balance of power.

I should have followed Route 48 up the Kattegat but I didn't, I just set a parallel course to take us outside the island of Laeso, then slammed right across the Bøchers and Tønneberg Banks with the white water kicking high under *Venturer*'s stern and the spread of our wake breaking in great foaming waves against the rocks of Syrodde Point.

Eighty-four minutes later we rounded the Skaw and entered the Skagerrak. It was very dark by then with a cold mist lying over the surface of the water. We had a five hour run ahead of us up to The Naze.

And when we'd raised that we had another three hundred and ninety sea miles to steam until the earliest position where both McReadie and I agreed we could leave her. In fact, earlier on in the day we started to think we still had a chance of getting away with it – because at twenty-four knots it meant we still had nearly twelve hours left to get clear of the ship before she detonated.

Until the BBC weatherman had said, quite positively, 'Gale Warning for sea areas Forties, Fair Isle, Faeroes and Iceland . . . Winds north-easterly, force eight to nine . . .'

Which meant our twenty-four would be reduced to a slamming, pounding fifteen knots, and we wouldn't be able to abandon *Venturer* for another ten hours out of our indescribably precious twelve. Not that we really felt it would be worthwhile by then. I mean, you just can't get very far in a three-knot-going-downhill ship's lifeboat. Not when you've only got an estimated two hours to do it in.

McReadie said resignedly, 'You take 'em away in the boat, chum. Personally – for the sake of only being a good spit away from that bloody obscenity when it blows – I'm for just staying warm and dry aboard an' trying to drink myself to death first.'

But McReadie always was a pessimist. For my part I fully intended to try swimming away if there wasn't any faster transport. But it didn't really seem to matter – I was too tired to be frightened any longer. I turned away from where we'd been talking in low tones, grouped like sea moths around the somehow friendly glow of the binnacle, and stumbled out into the cold rawness of the night.

Leaning over the after end of the wing I stared miserably towards the poop, watching the slow roll of the mast against the fractionally lighter grey of the sky and feeling the tremble of the ship beneath me as she raced nearer and nearer to her last resting place – already plotted by a fine black course line on the chart, with a neatly drawn circle at the end of it and the revised, pencilled notation, '*ETA* 02.46 *hours GMT*'.

And then – nothing.

The stern heaved sullenly as a wave, larger than the rest, caught her and rolled aft along our sides. The starboard lifeboats hung forlornly in their davits, great white ghosts commanding an empty boat-deck. Just for a moment I stared along it, and remembered what it had been like the last time I'd left *Venturer*, with the old boats pounded to shattered matchwood by that Red destroyer's fire, and the colandered ventilators gaping with dead eyes, and Mike Ritchie exploding in a red bloody haze while I was trying to claw to my feet and screaming frantically to young Twist, 'Meet her! F'r Chrissakes, *meet* her . . .!' because she'd over-ridden the automatic pilot and was swinging crazily across . . .

. . . the *auto* pilot!

I started running back to the wheelhouse, to where the others were staring at me in amazement. But I didn't give a damn even if they did think Cable's mind had finally snapped.

I just blurted, 'McReadie, you heroic sod, you're going to do without that last drink, boy. 'Cause you're going for a boat ride with the rest of us . . . an' there's just a faint chance you may even live through it.'

Down below my feet, a long way below, a white and red counter said 'One hundred and thirty-seven minutes to zero'.

I stared bitterly out over the black, heaving waters of the Norwegian Sea, ducking involuntarily as a white-streaked wave battered angrily against *Venturer*'s flaring, slicing bow then curled back over the bridge in a fine blown spray of icy mist. It was ironic, really, that the only goddamn thing to go according to plan since we'd started OPERATION STAYSAIL was that the gale had arrived exactly as promised by the BBC man. And it had increased steadily over the long, grey day we'd just suffered until, only now when it was far too late, it had decreased slightly.

It still wasn't a night to abandon a ship in. But, then

again, no night ever is!

The Second Mate stepped out of the wheelhouse and called quietly, 'Thirteen minutes to go, sir. Before we're on station.'

I peered at my watch in the eternal, colourless half-light of the northern night. It meant that we would then have one hundred and twenty-four minutes left before the whole of our oceanic world evaporated in a column of steam and spray with such a force and energy that only the sea itself could match it. Except I was a seaman, and I knew the sea. But I didn't know, and couldn't cope with, the violence of a radio-active colossus.

I nodded. 'Automàtic pilot set, Mister Twist?'

He smiled tightly, almost apologetically. 'I put her over on to it half an hour ago, sir. Seeing we're going to be leaving her in a bit of a hurry.'

I couldn't help grinning back. Twist had just made the understatement of the century. I said, 'Better get your life-jacket on then. Oh, and secure the ship's log in an oilskin. We'll take it with us . . .'

He turned back into the wheelhouse and I called, '. . . Twist.'

The kid looked back. 'Sir?'

I said awkwardly, 'Thanks, Mister. For volunteering to come when you did.'

He smiled again, uncertainly, and I felt very sad as I watched his slim form silhouetted against the chartroom door. You see, I knew we didn't have a chance. Not against the bomb, and not even after my idea of employing the automatic pilot to steer *Venturer* away from where we'd planned to abandon her, and thereby give us that extra margin of sea room that we so desperately needed to survive.

Oh sure, the Chief had been working throughout the day to rig up what he called his 'Wee Springy Thingy', and was really an ingenious tensioning device which would slowly open the throttles right up while we, in theory, took to the boat and sat back while *Venturer* steamed into the dawn with a gyroscopic hand on the wheel and a robot hand on the engine controls.

It was a great conception. It meant we'd converted *British Venturer* into the biggest thermo-nuclear guided missile in the world . . . except for the fuses in the demolition charges laid along her keel.

Because they had a fixed maximum setting of twenty minutes. And not all the ingenuity of the best Marine assault engineers in the business could add one extra minute of life to them once they were activated.

So *Venturer* would lie placidly on the bottom of the sea, just waiting for the counter to reach zero, while we bucketed around on the surface in a lifeboat that would need a miracle even to keep it afloat, never mind claw futilely for more southing – until that bloody obscenity erupted less than ten miles from us.

And we were screaming from the bottom of, maybe, a three hundred foot, boiling tidal wave . . .

McReadie hauled himself over the top of the ladder and said bitterly, 'Bloody Nazis!'

I pulled myself into the present and frowned disinterestedly. 'Bloody who?'

'Nazis! Or, to be specific – Kleiber! He's just twigged we're heading north instead've down to the UK. Then he got a bit upset because all De'Ath's boys are wearing life-jackets . . . nervous bastard.'

I had to grin. 'Wait 'till he gets the sixty thousand dollar message. About the bomb. He's going to wish he was back in an MVD jail. What did you tell him we intended to do, anyway?'

'That if he didn't stop yelling I'd put him over the soddin' wall with a set of firebars for boots!' McReadie snarled brutally. It hadn't been quite what I'd meant, but we all had our problems right then.

I looked aft through the darkness towards number two motor boat. McReadie had been supervising her preparation and I could dimly see that the cover had been stripped off and that she was ready swung out, secured only by a strop to prevent her from smashing against the davits as we rolled.

I said, 'Everything ready to go?'

He glanced at me and, just for a moment, I saw his eyes soften slightly. 'It's no use, is it, Brev?'

I shrugged. 'No. But by God, I'm too scared to give up trying, Mac . . .'

Twist stepped from the wheelhouse. 'It's time, sir. We should be in position now.'

McReadie punched me gently on the shoulder. 'We'll need two minutes to prepare the fuses, then I'll clear the engine-room. And she is still your ship . . .' I could sense the sympathy in his voice, and the understanding, '. . . Captain.'

I watched him slide down the ladder to the boat-deck, then I turned away and walked across the wide bridge to the wheelhouse. For the very last time.

Just for one brief, indescribably precious moment I let my hand rest on the smooth brass casing of the telegraphs. Then I gripped them and swung. Back, then to the vertical. 'STOP BOTH ENGINES.'

The vibration cut almost immediately below my feet and I just stood there and felt the ship move, eerily silent, as we coasted along with the white-capped waves rearing ghostly, pallid fingers above the line of the windows.

Sensing a movement behind I turned to see Twist, hugely chested in an orange kapok lifejacket. He coughed diffidently and held out a second one. 'Your preserver, sir . . . It's time to go.'

Preserve what, Twist? Preserve **Brevet** Cable for another hundred and twenty minutes just so's he can be scalded alive in a tormented, steaming ocean . . .?

I said stiffly, 'Thank you, Mister Twist. My compliments to Lieutenant De'Ath and tell him that, if he would be good enough to assist you in lowering the boat to centrecastle-deck level, then his men can board her from there.'

The kid nodded. 'Aye, aye, sir!'

'And . . . Twist.'

'Sir?'

'The sea's running too high to use the pilot ladder. See the boat's griped well into the rails and wait for me to join you. Oh, and keep a weather eye on Kleiber. He may prove a bit . . . ah . . . difficult.'

I followed him to the top of the ladder then turned back, just for a last look. There wasn't long, in fact there wasn't any time at all because McReadie's crowd would be up on deck and the fuses already burning away the minutes of living time . . . but the ship seemed so terribly deserted and forlorn, with the gusting wind wailing dolefully in the shrouds and the now useless, empty eyes of the radar scanner whirling round and round and round in the grey half-light. And the black, rolling funnel swinging against the torn clouds above. It was a good choice though, was black – almost as if the ship was wearing a crépe band in mourning for what might have been, between us.

Time to go. They'd be waiting for me. In that bloody little boat . . .

And then it started shrieking. The engine-room telephone. Sounding like a shocked cry of terror in the night. While I just stared at it in utter, disbelieving horror. Because there never should have been anybody down there any longer.

Not by now.

Nine

The phone shrilled again, then stopped abruptly. For another few precious seconds I just stood at the head of the ladder and stared into the empty wheelhouse, and listened to the squeak of the davit blocks as the now invisible boat moved fractionally against the rails below. Then I ran urgently back across the wing and snatched the receiver off its hook.

'Bridge!'

But the only sound I could hear was the gentle purring of a cat. Then I realized that it wasn't a cat at all, that it was the throb of the huge diesels as they turned over in neutral, waiting for the Chief's Springy Thingy to ease them back up to full power ahead. *After* we'd gone.

And there was another thing which was even more disturbing – that I could actually hear those engines, which meant the telephone was still off its hook down there. And, if it was, then why weren't they answering, f'r . . .

I shouted, '*Bridge!* This is the Captain. Goddammit! Who's down there . . .?'

Nothing! The bulkhead clock said seven minutes had now passed since we'd stopped.

I started to run for the ladder and then – quite ridiculously – spun back and carefully hung the bridge receiver back on its hook. It just seemed to be the tidy, seamanlike thing to do at the time, until I remembered the bomb.

The scene in the starboard centrecastle alleyway was like a monochrome image straight out of hell. Except there was water instead of fire, and there was colour in the bright orange lifejackets hampering the men in the boat. Twist stood in the stern trying desperately to hold his balance as

196

he fitted the tiller into the rudderpost, while De'Ath and two Marines held the boat with rope gripes against the rails and another two men stood by the falls, ready to let go.

I skidded to a halt. One of the soldiers was right up in the bow of the boat, and if the after falls carried away then the stern would plummet and the bow would snap back against the ropes to crush him like a high-speed power press . . . I roared, 'Get inboard, you bloody man! *Inboard* of the falls!'

Then I realized it didn't make the slightest difference anyway, because if she went down in this sea he wouldn't be any deader than the rest of them – only a bit luckier, because it wouldn't take quite as long as drowning.

I half ducked as a sea, black and roaring, smashed against the hull and sent a barrage of near-solid spray across the alleyway, then shouted at Twist, 'Where's Mister McReadie? And the rest of the crew?'

Another wall of water reared above the rail and slammed me against the bulkhead while Twist stared back white faced, which didn't surprise me a bit because he must have been almost as terrified of launching into that sea as I was. 'Still below, sir! With the Chief and . . .'

The rest of his words were lost in a splashing, gurgling torrent pouring back through the scuppers. I spat convulsively and screamed, 'I'll go! An' you take the boat away yourself if we're not back within . . .'

Then I was knocked backwards again under a black and green and white surge, and I came up yelling 'Ahhhhhhh, *fuck* it . . .!' because I knew he would never leave without us anyway. Somehow I lurched along the alleyway and wrenched the engine-room door open just in time for the next roll of the ship to propel me across the coaming and into the dazzling bright glare of the cathedral space within.

This time everything seemed pleasantly warm and quiet and orderly compared to the shrieking storm outside. I felt terribly, hopelessly tired and, just for a moment, I thought about how nice it would be to lie down on the softly gleaming oil sheen of the plates and go to sleep. And never know when the millisecond came for *Venturer* to die.

It was a long way, forcing myself down to the bottom of those bottomless, shiny ladders. A long, frightening, anticipatory way.

I hit the control platform with my heart somewhere up around my ears and the nervous tic leaping uncontrollably. I shouted, 'Right, McReadie, what's the . . .'

Then stopped shouting because there wasn't anyone down there to listen. Which was exactly like it had been the first time I was down here, only that had all been explained already, and Horst Geber was as dead as anybody ever could be with twenty or thirty 7.92 millimetre *Kurz* rounds in the tummy . . . But *someone* had phoned from here, and only a few minutes ago.

And then I saw the body.

It was sprawled on its back under the still swinging telephone receiver. Oh, dear God, please don't let it be . . . McReadie. I felt the ship sway crazily about me, and it wasn't only the waves, then I descended another few steps and looked down at the face, but I didn't learn any more from doing that because the bullet must have entered from the back of the head and . . .

It was only while I was gagging convulsively that I noticed the forlornly upturned feet. And I knew who it was, then. Because they were encased in large, still shiny black boots. And they'd trodden on me quite often in the back of a madly careering lorry.

They told me my big Corporal never would get to finish that paperback he'd been reading all that time ago in the sky . . .

I'd made it to exactly half-way down the next run of ladders to the deep tank bulkhead and the bomb before I saw McReadie, the Chief and the other Marine AE staring up at me, obviously a bit shattered by the panic-accelerated violence of my descent.

When – quite inexplicably – McReadie shouted, 'Get back, Cable! Before he . . .'

And, too late, I saw Paulus Kleiber whirling round from where he'd been concealed by the overhang of the platform. I remember even thinking stupidly, 'That's funny, but why's *he* down here when he could be in the boat?'

Then I also saw the gun swinging up from where it had been covering the others, and the little voice of panic started screaming in my head, 'Look out, Cable boy! That mad bloody Nazi's goin' to cut you down no matter what you do . . . unless you can go straight in with your boots . . .'

So I just kept on running down the ladder towards him, with the muzzle of that horrifying Schmeisser trying desperately to follow my erratically bounding figure. Then Kleiber got panicky, too, squeezed the trigger too soon and I was falling, falling under a shrieking, spanging canopy of ricocheting lead. But I knew, with cold detachment, that I still wasn't going to make it in time. Not before he'd chopped me to bloody tatters to match Geber and the two hoods.

I hit the steel plates with a crash which probably broke every bone in my body – not that it really mattered anyway, seeing he was going to do precisely that, and in about ten millionths of a second. Christ but I could even *see* down the barrel of his sub-machine-gun, with the cordite smoke still curling from it after that last burst, and it was the third time that night I'd looked into a gun from that nerve-tearing angle and, though this one was a lot smaller than the T54, it was also a bloody sight more personal.

And more immediately deadly.

I closed my eyes and wished I hadn't come. Not even for McReadie.

There was only the one shot. It didn't even seem to hurt much, really. Then nothing else seemed to be happening so I opened them again, thinking, 'If the silly bastard's missed at *that* range, an' jammed his gun at the same time, then he doesn't deserve to . . .'

Kleiber stared down at me with an expression of such utter regret that it made me wonder if he hadn't changed his mind about killing me. Then he took a slow, hesitant step backwards while the Schmeisser fell out of his hands, and I saw that it wasn't so much him changing his mind as that he didn't have one left to change. Because someone seemed to have shot *him* first instead and there wasn't any top to his skull anymore . . .

McReadie bounded up the ladder the very moment after Kleiber had fallen down it. I don't think I've ever seen anyone looking quite so sick with apprehension as he did right then. Not until he saw I was still alive and swearing, anyway. Then, almost comically, his expression mutated to one of intense disgust while he waved a gun at me and snapped, 'Silly suicidal idiot, goin' for him like that! Though you did give me the chance to snatch this up, I must admit.'

I started to shake uncontrollably with the delayed reaction, but I didn't go and spoil his image of Cable's Fifth Cavalry arrival by telling him I actually *fell* down those bloody ladders, and anyway I was too busy staring up at the gun he'd used. I'd seen it before – it was a Browning High Power automatic. Made in Belgium. And the hole in the deceased *Hauptmann* Kleiber's cranium proved for once and for all that Geber hadn't been bluffing that time.

I grated savagely, 'Just two things, McReadie! Like why was he holding you up, f'r one?'

'He used his eyes, saw what was going on, and decided he didn't want to go for a lifeboat ride while we blew the bottom out of the ship. Of course we weren't carrying weapons down here, not now, so the Corporal tried to warn you . . .' McReadie shrugged expressively, then nodded dispassionately down at the crumpled Kleiber, '. . . he never did find out the reason we couldn't have taken him to Norway. Not even if he'd had all the guns in the bloody world at our heads.'

'And the charges? How long have we got?'

He smiled wistfully. 'Still forty minutes – the fuses haven't been activated yet. But for the big bang . . .? Maybe just over an hour an' a half now . . . plus the time it takes a tidal wave to travel less than ten miles.'

And even I didn't think it was worth hurrying. Not any more.

We got the boat away. God knows how, in that sea, but we did. Maybe the oil we'd spread helped a little. I only remember standing aft at the tiller while the Chief cranked the starter, then I'd waited until a great, sullenly viscous wave rose to meet us in time with the roll of the ship, and bellowed, 'Leggo falls . . .! Fend off forr'ad!'

And we'd hit the water with a thunderous crash and a spray of almost pure diesel scum as Reid slammed her into gear, then we were sheering away, bucketing uncontrollably as the high, rust-streaked sides of the deserted ship towered over us and the Marines staring up at her with faces only a little whiter than those of the professional seamen among us . . .

. . . until, suddenly, we were riding easily with the wind howling unchecked over the crests of the waves and flaying our already salt-encrusted features until we fell twenty feet into the temporary peace of the trough. And we came up once more towards the scudding dawn sky, and Twist shouted, 'She's going, sir! She's under power again!'

Miserably I watched my ship steam away from me, and felt all dead and cold inside. Though maybe just a little proud as well, because she was sailing her last few miles like the arrogant, lovely bitch that she was – with the white water kicking high under her rounded counter and the flare of her bows haughtily crushing and buffeting the sensual, lascivious fingers of the sea.

She was a full mile away before we took our eyes off her.

And saw the other ship.

I remember how we just sat in the boat, and clung to the

gunwales with incredulously turned heads, and took great, thirsty looks at the stranger as she rampaged through the scudding spindrift on a course to bring her right over us.

Then we hung on the next crest just long enough for me to make out the slim, rapacious lines of her, with the black gleaming windows sectioning her grey, armoured bridge and the streamlined cube of her forward gun turret trained fore and aft. And I knew that she was exactly the same as those Soviet destroyers Twist and I had watched so bitterly as they circled *British Venturer* in another sea a million years ago.

I started to laugh, because it *was* bloody ironic, really. After five hundred miles of waiting for them, and sailing openly and blithely through their very own Baltic Sea – and now we were all back to Square One, where it had all started. But I wasn't frightened any more, because I'd already lost my ship for ever . . .

I stood up in the lurching, spiralling boat and grinned fiercely. 'You're too late, you bastards! You're far too bloody late . . .'

Until McReadie started waving his arms like a schoolkid, and yelling, 'Jesus, but she's flying the White Ensign! She's a frigate, Cable . . . She's a goddamned beautiful Royal Navy frigate!'

But I never was much good. Not when it came to differentiating between armoured peas in an international pod.

I hauled myself up to the top of the scrambling net they'd prepared and swung my aching, oil-soaked body over the rail. The first thing I noticed was a tiddly little brass plate screwed to the immaculate bulkhead – HMS *Afghan*. Which was odd, because I knew I'd already heard that name before. Somewhere. But we didn't have a lot of time for reminiscences. In fact, I still didn't really know if we had any time at all.

I saw an officer approaching who looked as though he might be the first mate or lieutenant or whatever of this taxpayer's bucket, but McReadie beat me to the punch. He snapped imperiously, 'My name's McReadie – Commander McReadie, Royal Navy! And that ship over there . . .'

The embryo Drake listened, a bit distantly I thought, until McReadie had finished. '. . . and I estimate we have fifty-eight minutes left to steam south before she detonates. You will please be good enough to advise the Captain immediately.'

I didn't hear if there was anything more. I was too busy staring at our bows as we swung further and further *north*, steadying precisely on the now five miles distant silhouette of *British Venturer*. And – disbelievingly – I became aware of the steadily increasing vibrations of the gas turbines below as they forced the revolutions up to full power.

And as we started to *chase* the floating hydrogen bomb I'd just abandoned.

While the First Lieutenant said, with the most gentlemanly but utterly devastating contempt I'd ever heard, 'Really, McReadie – *if* that is your correct name. When we first raised you on radar and realized you had stopped we naturally guessed that something was amiss. That's why we're here to investigate . . . But when we also see a curiously small party abandoning an obviously well found vessel in the middle of the ocean . . . well, I mean there's only one reasonable conclusion we can arrive at, surely?'

McReadie ground dangerously, 'And what's that, Mister?'

'That your story is only partly true. I state a purely hypothetical, but much more probable, solution . . .' The Lieutenant shrugged wisely and continued like a learned judge, '. . . that there are indeed demolition charges laid aboard that ship – but that you have merely been caught red-handed while perpetrating a not entirely original act to defraud your insurers. That you have, say, a virtually valueless cargo which will naturally – after the loss – appreciate by a very great amount in your claim . . .'

McReadie said – very, very deliberately, 'You great, fantasy-brained, gold-ringed, brass-bound suicidal fu . . .!'

I looked at my watch through its film of diesel. We only had fifty-two minutes now. I yelled, 'F'r Christ's sake, man! That's *British Venturer* out there. You *must* have read the bloody papers, even you.'

He nodded stiffly. 'Exactly! And so does our captain . . . which means we're perfectly aware that the real *Venturer* is – apart from being impounded in an East German port at this moment – also badly damaged on her starboard side boat-deck. And that her funnel livery is that of her BMSNC owners – which is not black. And that she most certainly does *not* sail under the Panamanian Flag.'

I muttered weakly, 'So what d'you intend to do now?'

He smiled in a terribly British way. 'We will lay alongside her and attempt to board while she is still steaming. Our gunnery staff will then repair below and defuse the charges in any bombs they find . . . they are extremely competent.'

I watched the gap close between us and *Venturer*. Competent they would bloody need to be!

We were within a mile of her when she finally went.

The First Lieutenant had escorted us to the bridge to await the Captain's displeasure but, before we could enter, I heard De'Ath say 'My God!' and I turned just in time to see the last moments of my ship.

She didn't even falter for a few, proud seconds. She just kept on racing at twenty-four knots with the spray curling back over her long fore-deck and the great sweep of the bows dipping and rising into the seas. Then the chain of explosions rumbled towards us over the water and she curtseyed a little with the pain of it, until her fo'c'sle dug deeper as she started to roll over and I watched the white, foaming waves rush greedily aft to smash in her forward hatch covers and break in huge, roaring gouts against the white centrecastle.

And I was squeezing the grey-painted rails separating us while she lay further and further over until her sad black funnel was still, incredibly, smashing through the tops of the waves. I retained one last, agonized memory of her deck plan with the boats tumbling vertically, and the bridge I'd been so proud of crumbling to varnished matchwood.

Then she was gone, still driving doggedly under the surface of the Norwegian Sea . . . and I felt so lonely and tired. And hopeless.

Until a man with two and a half rings on his sleeve stepped angrily from the frigate's bridge and bellowed, 'You damned pirates! Doing that to a ship . . .'

Then halted abruptly, with an expression of incredulity on his florid, aquiline features. And gasped weakly, 'Commander . . . Commander *McReadie*, sir! But what in God's name . . . ?'

While McReadie grated, 'Flapper! Flapper bloody Evans! Dammit but you always were a dense little bastard. Even when you were my Number One in *Tormentor!*'

While the First Lieutenant – who must really have been a very quick lad behind the veneer – just gave one leap for the frigate's broadcast system microphone and snapped, 'All hands! This is not an exercise – I say again, this is *not* an exercise . . . Assume State One, Condition Zulu Alfa. Nuclear attack imminent . . . NBCD Headquarters staff, close up! Special sea dutymen, close up! Fire and repair parties . . .'

We screamed round in a racing, stern drifting half-circle. McReadie fought the centrifugal pull while I saw him gazing at me with the white teeth bright in the black, oil-covered face. It was the old McReadie grin and – just for a few moments – we laughed at each other like idiot children. Because we knew there might still be time. Just enough time . . .

I leaned over the vibrating rail and gazed wistfully astern. There wasn't anything left to remember, except perhaps a spreading, silvery oilstain on the heaving waters of the Norwegian Sea. But it didn't really matter, now. She'd already gone from me forever.

Something else seemed to fade from my side right then,

and I knew I'd also parted company with an old, and now perhaps, very understanding acquaintance. Because my ghost had gone, too. My old, one-legged Russian sea captain . . .

I thought, 'What a silly thing for a rugged sailorman like me – Brevet Cable – to be doing . . . to be crying. Like this.'